PLANE STRAIN CRACK TOUGHNESS TESTING OF HIGH STRENGTH METALLIC MATERIALS

by William F. Brcwn, Jr., and John E. Srawley

ASTM SPECIAL TECHNICAL PUBLICATION NO. 410

List price $5.50; 30 per cent discount to members

published by the
AMERICAN SOCIETY FOR TESTING AND MATERIALS
1916 Race Street, Philadelphia, Pa. 19103

in cooperation with the
NATIONAL AERONAUTICS AND
SPACE ADMINISTRATION

NOTE

The Society is not responsible, as a body,
for the statements and opinions
advanced in this publication.

Printed in Baltimore, Md.
December, 1967

Foreword

The objective of this report is to present a state-of-the-art survey of the analytical and experimental basis for determination of the plane strain crack toughness of metallic materials. It is anticipated that the information presented will serve as a basis for formulating recommended practices for K_{Ic} testing.

This publication is a cooperative effort of ASTM and NASA. Most of the data contained here were obtained at the NASA-Lewis Research Center as part of a NASA-NRL Cooperative Program for Plane Strain Fracture Toughness Testing. By cooperating with ASTM in publication of this information, NASA is helping to fulfill its obligation to provide the widest practicable and appropriate dissemination of the results from its research activities.

This publication was prepared for ASTM Committee E-24 on Fracture Testing of Metals as the first report of Subcommittee I on High Strength Metallic Materials. The authors are with NASA Lewis Research Center, Cleveland, Ohio. The members of the subcommittee are: G. E. Pellissier (chairman), U. S. Steel Corp.; C. D. Beachem, U. S. Naval Research Laboratory; W. F. Brown, Jr., NASA Lewis Research Center; J. E. Campbell, Battelle Memorial Inst.; T. J. Dolan, University of Illinois; R. H. Heyer, Armco Steel Corp.; J. H. Hodge, U. S. Steel Corp.; G. R. Irwin, U. S. Naval Research Laboratory; J. G. Kaufman, Alcoa Research Laboratory; J. M. Krafft, U. S. Naval Research Laboratory; F. R. Larson, Watertown Arsenal; J. R. Low, Jr., General Electric Co. Research Laboratory; P. C. Paris, Lehigh University; J. E. Srawley, NASA Lewis Research Center; C. F. Tiffany, Boeing Co.; and Volker Weiss, Syracuse University.

Related
ASTM Publications

Flow and Fracture of Metals and Alloys in Nuclear Environments, STP 380 (1965), $24.00

Fracture Toughness Testing and Its Applications, STP 381 (1965), $19.50

Contents

Introduction 1
Fundamentals of Specimen Design and Testing 2
  Popin K_{Ic} Measurements with Flat Plate Specimens 5
K Calibrations of Specimens 8
  Adjustment of Two-Dimensional K Calibrations 8
  Methods for K Calibration 9
  Center-Cracked Plate Under Uniform Tension 11
  Double-Edge-Cracked Plate 11
  Single-Edge-Cracked Plate Specimens 11
  Single-Edge-Cracked Plates in Tension 12
  Single-Edge-Cracked Bend Specimens 13
  Crackline Loaded Single-Edge-Cracked Specimen 14
  Circumferentially Cracked Round Bar 15
Specimen Size Requirements 16
  Crack Length Requirement 20
  Thickness Requirement 23
  Ligament Requirement 25
  Summary of Suggested Size Requirements 25
  Variability of K_{Ic} Results 26
Practical Specimen Types 27
  Recommended Specimen Dimensions and Corresponding Load Re-
    quirements 28
  Considerations in Selecting Specimens for Particular Applications .. 29
  Surface-Crack Specimen 30
  Cracked Charpy Specimens 33
Instrumentation 34
  Displacement Measurements 34
  Electric Potential Measurements 37
  Acoustic Emission 40
  Comparison of Methods 40
Criteria for Analysis of Load-Displacement Records 41
  Types of Load-Displacement Records 42
  Criteria and Data Analysis 44
Specimen Preparation and Testing 46
  Fatigue Crack Starter Notches 46
  Fatigue Cracking 48
  Face Grooving 51
  Pin Friction Effects in Bending 53
Appendixes
  I—Basis for the Analysis of Load-Displacement Records 56
  II—Specimen Types 60
  III—Notation 62
References 63
Discussion 66

(Discussers and page numbers: M. J. Manjoine, 66; E. J. Ripling,
70; W. K. Wilson, 75; C. E. Feddersen, 77; H. P. Chu, 79; G. M.
Orner and B. S. Lement, 82; J. G. Kaufman, 86; R. H. Heyer, 86;
P. N. Randall, 88; S. R. Novak and S. T. Rolfe, 126)

William F. Brown, Jr., and John E. Srawley

Plane Strain Crack Toughness Testing of High Strength Metallic Materials

Introduction

This report deals with the design and testing of crack-notched specimens for determination of the resistance of high strength metallic materials to unstable opening-mode crack extension under plane strain conditions. Test methods concerned with subcritical crack extension due to repeated loading or aggressive environments are not discussed. It is assumed that the reader will be familiar with the terminology and concepts of linear elastic fracture mechanics used in earlier reports of ASTM Committee E-24 on Fracture Testing of Metals [1–5].[1] Much of the background has been thoroughly reviewed recently [6].

The plane strain crack toughness K_{Ic} is a material property which is measured in terms of the opening-mode stress intensity factor K_I, expressed in units of (stress) $\times$ (length)$^{1/2}$. The distinction between K_{Ic} and K_I is important, and is comparable to the distinction between strength and stress. To determine a K_{Ic} value, a crack-notched specimen of suitable dimensions is increasingly loaded until the crack becomes unstable and extends abruptly. The ratio of K_I to the applied load is a function of specimen design and dimensions which is evaluated by stress analysis, as discussed later. The K_I value corresponding to the load at which unstable crack extension is observed is the K_{Ic} value determined in the test. This property is a function of temperature and strain rate.

The plane strain crack toughness of a given sample of material is characterized by the distribution of K_{Ic} values determined on specimens taken from the sample. The dispersion of this distribution is often considerable, and the K_{Ic} levels of engineering significance should be the lower confidence limits rather than mean values to introduce conservatism into subsequent analyses.

Under certain conditions the K_{Ic} level of a material can be used

---

[1] The italic numbers in brackets refer to the list of references at the end of this report.

to estimate the load that a structural member containing a crack of specified dimensions could sustain without fracture. Strength estimates based on K_{Ic} assume a high degree of constraint to plastic flow of the material at the crack tip, corresponding to a state of plane strain. Under different conditions, such as those pertaining to a through-thickness crack in a thin plate, the ability of the material to resist unstable extension of the crack can be substantially greater than indicated by the K_{Ic} level. The effective toughness then depends upon the degree of relaxation of crack front constraint due to the proximity of the plate surfaces.

The effective toughness of a material is not expected to be less than its K_{Ic} level under any practical conditions, and it is therefore appropriate to regard K_{Ic} as a basic index of intrinsic crack toughness. It has been established that the K_{Ic} levels of a number of structural materials are essentially independent of specimen design and dimensions when the specifications for valid K_{Ic} testing are met.

It is necessary to develop specifications for valid K_{Ic} testing because real materials do not deform in the elastic-brittle manner assumed in linear elastic fracture mechanics. Nevertheless, when a sufficiently large crack-notched specimen is tested, the behavior is sufficiently close to elastic brittle because the crack tip plastic region remains small relative to the significant specimen dimensions. The conditions for valid K_{Ic} testing comprise both minimum limits for specimen dimensions and a maximum limit on deviation from linearity of the load-displacement record. These limits are established on the basis of test data obtained for the purpose, as discussed in subsequent sections. It should be clearly understood, however, that a certain degree of arbitrariness is unavoidable in specifying these limits. As the amount of useful data increases it should be possible to reduce the degree of arbitrariness in setting the conditions for valid K_{Ic} testing.

Fundamentals of Specimen Design and Testing

The purpose of this section is to review certain basic factors in the design and testing of K_{Ic} specimens. To understand the important factors in the design of practical K_{Ic} test specimens it is useful to start out by considering a configuration that is as simple as possible.

The simplest configuration to consider is the axially symmetric circular crack located inside a body sufficiently large that the effects of its bounding surfaces on the stress field of the crack are negligible. Initially, before load is applied to the body, the crack is regarded as ideally sharp and free from any self-equilibrating stress field (such as might exist in a practical specimen from the residual effects of artificially generating the crack). The "specimen" is tested by steadily increasing the gross tensile stress, σ, which is applied remote from and normal to the crack plane.

The opening mode stress intensity at every point around the crack border is given by

$$K_I = 2\sigma \, (a/\pi)^{1/2} \dots \dots \dots \dots \dots (1)$$

where $2a$ is the effective crack diameter. When σ is small compared with the yield strength of the material, σ_{YS}, the effective crack diameter is not appreciably different from the actual crack diameter $2a_0$. Strictly, however, the effective crack diameter is taken to be formally equal to $2a_0 + K_I^2/3\pi\sigma_{YS}^2$, where the supplemental term is Irwin's estimate of the plane strain plastic zone correction term for matching an equivalent elastic crack to an elastic-plastic crack [7].

To conduct a satisfactory K_{Ic} test it is necessary to provide for autographic recording of the applied load versus the output from a trans-

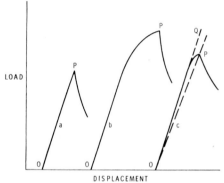

FIG. 1—*Hypothetical load-displacement plots for tests of circular crack specimens.*

ducer which accurately senses some quantity which can be related to extension of the crack. The basic measurement for this purpose is the relative displacement of two points located symmetrically on opposite sides of the crack plane. Assuming that such a measurement could be made on a buried-crack specimen, the displacement per unit load would be constant as long as the effective crack diameter remained constant but would increase if $2a$ increased. Hence, the load-displacement plot would be linear as long as there was no appreciable change in $2a$. In the ideal case in which $2a_0$ is large compared with the quantity $(K_{Ic}/\sigma_{YS})^2$, the load-displacement plot would be linear up to the point at which the specimen fractured abruptly, as in Fig. 1a. The value of K_{Ic} could then be calculated from the maximum load and the measured crack diameter, using Eq 1.

It follows from Eq 1 that if $2a_0$ were less than about $1.5(K_{Ic}/\sigma_{YS})^2$, the applied stress would exceed σ_{YS} before the stress intensity reached K_{Ic}. The specimen would then undergo gross plastic deformation before fracture, and the load-displacement plot would be obviously nonlinear, as in Fig. 1b. It is likely that fracture would nevertheless occur rather abruptly without much crack extension prior to maximum load, but since the crack stress field could no longer be matched by that of an equivalent elastic crack with an acceptable degree of accuracy, the K_I value which could be calculated formally from the maximum load should not be regarded as a valid K_{Ic}.

The crack diameter is the characteristic dimension of the simple specimen under discussion. This characteristic dimension has to exceed a certain size, proportional to $(K_{Ic}/\sigma_{YS})^2$, in order for a valid K_{Ic} measurement to be made. The quantity $(K_{Ic}/\sigma_{YS})^2$ is a characteristic property of the material having dimensions of length which is, in some respects, a better measure of crack toughness than K_{Ic}. The useful lower limit of the crack diameter cannot be deduced, at present, from theoretical

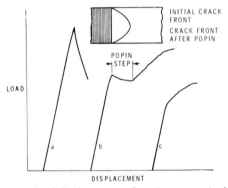

FIG. 2—*Schematic load-displacement plots for tests of plate specimens.*

considerations alone; it must be established empirically from the results of a large number of trial K_{Ic} tests.

In a test in which $2a_0$ is greater than, but close to, the useful lower limit, the load-displacement record might be somewhat nonlinear near to the point of maximum load, as in Fig. 1c. In fact, records of this sort are often encountered in valid tests of practical specimens. The nonlinearity is partly due to slight, irregular extension of the crack during the last stages of loading and partly due to plastic deformation around the crack border (which can be regarded formally as a virtual crack extension). If the extent of the nonlinearity is not excessive, then it can be ignored, and the K_{Ic} value can be calculated from the maximum load and the measured crack diameter $2a_0$. The question of how much nonlinearity is excessive needs to be specified precisely, of course, and it is consistent with the Irwin formalism to require that the allowable nonlinearity should not exceed that which would correspond to an increase of the initial crack diameter by the amount of the formal plane strain plastic zone correction term, in round figures: $0.1(K_{Ic}/\sigma_{YS})^2$.

It is shown later that this requirement leads to an equivalent limitation on the amount by which the reciprocal slope of the secant OP in Fig. 1c may exceed the reciprocal of the initial loading slope OQ if the test is to be regarded as valid.

Measurements of K_{Ic} with circular crack specimens are straightforward in principle. The same is true of related types of practical specimens, such as the crack-notch round bar (conceptually the inverse of the circular crack) or the surface crack specimen. Such specimens, however, are comparatively inefficient in respect of the volume of material and the magnitude of test load required for measurement of K_{Ic} of a given material. A number of different types of specimens of rectangular cross-section with through-thickness cracks, referred to

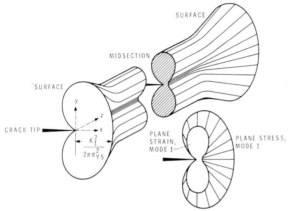

FIG. 3—*Formal representation of plastic zone at the front of a through-thickness crack in a plate.*

briefly as plate specimens, have been developed and are more efficient but conceptually more complicated. In the first place, the dimensions of the specimens in relation to the crack dimensions are not large enough that the effects of the specimen boundaries on the crack stress field can be neglected. This circumstance leads to more complicated expressions for K_I which are arrived at by either mathematical or experimental stress analysis, as discussed in the section on "K Calibrations of Specimens." Secondly, the most efficient use of these plate specimens depends upon the proper exploitation of the phenomenon of popin of the crack front which is observed when K_I reaches the K_{Ic} level of the material in plate specimens of nearly marginal thickness, as will now be explained.

Popin K_{Ic} Measurements with Flat Plate Specimens

The simplest type of plate specimen has a central, through-thickness crack of initial length $2a_0$ and is tested like the circular crack specimen by applying a uniformly distributed tensile load remote from the crack and normal to the crack plane. It can be regarded as a central, longitudinal slice of thickness B from a circular crack specimen, except that the crack fronts are assumed to be straight. If the width W is large compared to $2a_0$, then the opening mode stress intensity at every point along the crack fronts is:

$$K_I = \sigma(\pi a)^{1/2}\dots\dots\dots\dots\dots\dots\dots(2)$$

where σ is the gross applied stress and $2a$ is the effective crack length.

If $2a_0$ and B are both large compared with $(K_{Ic}/\sigma_{YS})^2$, then the test record, Fig. 2a, will be similar to that for a large circular crack specimen. If progressively thinner specimens are tested, however, a thickness range will be reached within which a specimen does not fracture completely at the load corresponding to K_{Ic}; instead, the abrupt advance of the crack front proceeds at the center but is suppressed at the free faces of the specimen. A tongue of fracture extends from the crack front, as shown schematically above Fig. 2b, and is then temporarily halted until the load is increased further. The test record, Fig. 2b, shows a popin step where the displacement increases without any commensurate increase in load. This popin phenomenon was first exploited by Boyle et al [8]; however, it should be noted that Boyle's specimens had sharp, machined notches that were not crack-tipped; consequently, the popins were more pronounced than they would have been if crack-notch specimens had been used, and the K_{Ic} values reported were somewhat higher.

The extent of the popin diminishes with decrease of specimen thickness, and the popin step in the test record becomes correspondingly less pronounced until it becomes impossible to detect the popin load with any degree of confidence, as in Fig. 2c. The popin phenomenon in a plate specimen is connected with the nature of the crack tip plastic zone in such a specimen, and it is useful to keep in mind certain aspects of this plastic zone. Figure 3 shows a formal representation of the shape of a crack tip plastic zone in a plate specimen, based on Mises yield limit lines for plane stress and plane strain as given by McClintock and Irwin [9]. The plastic zone shape which would be obtained by a more complicated elastic-plastic analysis would differ somewhat from this and would depend on the strain-hardening characteristics of the material. The differences, however, are not important for the present discussion. In a sufficiently thick specimen, plane strain conditions prevail in the middle part of the thickness, while plane stress conditions prevail near the faces. The plastic zone extends much further ahead of the crack near the faces than it does near midthickness, and the free surface influence extends into the thickness of the specimen for a distance which is proportional to $(K_I/\sigma_{YS})^2$. It is clear, therefore, that when the thickness is less than some critical value that is proportional to

$(K_{Ic}/\sigma_{YS})^2$, the constraint-relieving influence of the free faces will extend entirely through the thickness before the stress intensity reaches K_{Ic}. This relief of constraint tends to suppress opening-mode crack extension because of the increased possibilities of plastic deformation, and the effect of any opening-mode crack extension which does occur is masked by the effect of the concomitant plastic deformation. The result is a gradual, rather than abrupt, change in slope of the load-displacement record, as in Fig. 2c.

The lower limit of thickness for reliable popin K_{Ic} measurement cannot be predicted at present from theoretical considerations alone; it must be established from a sufficient number of trial K_{Ic} tests. Results that have been obtained for this purpose are discussed in the later section on "Specimen Size Requirements." While these results are not considered to be sufficient for final determination of the thickness

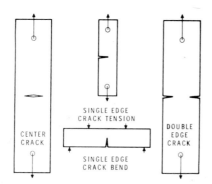

FIG. 4—*Some types of plate specimens for K_{Ic} testing.*

limit, they lead to the tentative conclusion that the thickness should not be less than about $2.5(K_{Ic}/\sigma_{YS})^2$. Results are also presented which lead to a similar conclusion regarding the crack length.

The wide center-cracked plate specimen thus has two independent characteristic dimensions, crack length and thickness, which must exceed certain sizes, proportional to the characteristic material property $(K_{Ic}/\sigma_{YS})^2$, in order that a valid K_{Ic} measurement can be made. A further improvement in specimen efficiency can be made by decreasing the specimen width W so that $2a_0/W$ is not a small fraction. When this is done Eq 2 no longer applies accurately; however, an appropriate stress analysis has been conducted, as discussed under "K Calibrations of Specimens." If $2a_0/W$ exceeds a certain value, a third independent characteristic dimension has to be considered, namely, the uncracked length, or ligament length, $W/2 - a_0$. Clearly, if the crack tip is too close to the free edge of the specimen, then the plastic zone size will be comparable to the ligament length, and it will no longer be possible to match the stress field with that of an equivalent elastic crack. Once again, the lower limit for $W/2 - a_0$ should be related to the characteristic material dimension $(K_{Ic}/\sigma_{YS})^2$, and the numerical proportion must be determined from trial K_{Ic} tests. At the present time there is insufficient data for anything more than an informed guess at this proportion.

These three independent characteristic dimensions have to be considered in designing any of the various types of plate specimens that are discussed in this report. The different types of plate specimens are shown schematically in Fig. 4, in approximate proportion for equal K_{Ic} measurement capacities, assuming that the thickness is adequate. These specimens are considered in detail in the sections which follow.

K Calibrations of Specimens

The crack tip stress intensity factor K_I in a test specimen is equal to the applied load multiplied by some function of the specimen dimensions, including the crack length, which depends on the specimen design. An established relation connecting K_I with the specimen dimensions and applied load for a particular design of specimen is called a K calibration for conciseness. Various methods of mathematical or experimental stress analysis are used to obtain K calibrations, and all the methods involve certain simplifying assumptions about the specimen configuration or the distribution of applied load or both. In making use of the resulting K calibrations it is advisable to be aware of these assumptions in order to avoid errors in K_{Ic} measurement that might result from incompatability of the K calibration with the design of the specimen and loading arrangements. This section is concerned with some pertinent aspects of various methods for K calibration and, in addition, includes the results of some extended or improved K calibrations that have become available since the preparation of Ref *10*.

Adjustment of Two-Dimensional K Calibrations

Apart from the crack-notch round bar, all the specimens considered in this section are plate specimens with through-thickness cracks. The cracks are assumed to have straight leading edges normal to the plate faces. Because of the difficulty of complete three-dimensional stress analysis, the K calibration procedures that are used, whether mathematical or experimental, treat these plate specimens as essentially two-dimensional. Some investigators adjust the two-dimensional K calibrations by multiplying by the factor $(1 - \nu^2)^{-1/2}$, where ν is Poisson's ratio. The magnitude of this adjustment factor is 1.05 when ν is 0.3. The adjustment is intended to improve the accuracy with which a two-dimensional K calibration would apply to a real plane strain crack toughness specimen and was used by the present authors in an earlier review paper [*10*]. It is by no means clear, however, that the adjustment factor should be as large as $(1 - \nu^2)^{-1/2}$, although there is general agreement that it should not be less than unity. In view of this uncertainty, the present authors now prefer the simpler alternative of using the two-dimensional K calibrations directly, without adjustment. Any error resulting from this practice will be small (probably less than 5 per cent) and conservative in that K_{Ic} will be underestimated rather than over-estimated.

Methods for K Calibration

The most commonly used experimental method of K calibration is that due to Irwin and Kies [11] in which measurements are made of the compliance (reciprocal of the stiffness) of a specimen having a narrow machined slot which is incrementally extended between successive measurements. The machined slot is used to simulate a crack primarily because it is not feasible to produce plane cracks of sufficient size and accuracy. It is apparent, however, that the compliance of a crack of given length will not be exactly the same as that of a finite-width slot of the same length. The experimental data are treated by expressing the specimen compliance as a function of crack length and then obtaining the derivative of this function with respect to crack length. While it is obvious that the compliance of a specimen with a slot will be somewhat greater than that of a specimen with an equally long crack, it does not follow that the derivative of the compliance with respect to the length will always be greater for the slot than for a crack. Since it is not known how to correct for the slot width, it is advisable to take the equivalent crack length as equal to the slot length but uncertain to the extent of the slot width. This uncertainty will be minimal if the specimen is made large and the slot narrow. It is always an advantage to use as large a specimen as possible for compliance measurements because the displacements will be proportionately large and can be measured with correspondingly good accuracy.

To conduct a compliance calibration with good accuracy it is necessary to use sensitive, accurate gages and to pay careful attention to detail [12, 13]. More accurate results can be obtained with compliant specimens, such as bend bars, than with stiff specimens, such as notched rounds. It should also be appreciated that the accuracy of the K calibration is likely to be less than that of the compliance measurements because of the differentiation operation required for reducing the experimental data. The error-magnifying effect of differentiation should be less the larger the number of compliance measurements involved for a given range of crack lengths.

The main advantage of the compliance calibration method is that the actual configuration and load distribution of a K_{Ic} test specimen can be closely modelled by the K calibration specimen. In a mathematical crack stress analysis the specimen has to be idealized into a sufficiently simple model. For instance, the complicated stress distribution around a loading pin has to be replaced by a simpler equivalent stress distribution assumed, on the basis of St. Venant's principle, to have the same effect on the crack stress field [*14–16*]. With careful attention to the design of both specimen and mathematical model, and apart from the fact that the model is usually two-dimensional, the inaccuracy due to the idealization can be made as small as desired. To achieve high ac-

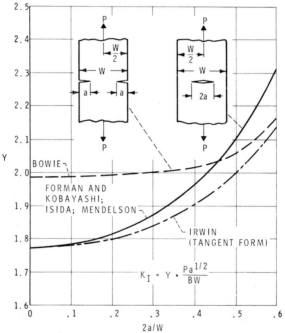

FIG. 5—*K calibrations for the center-cracked and double-edge-cracked specimens.*

curacy, however, may entail some sacrifice in compactness of the specimen design. For example, the length of a pin-loaded tension specimen might have to be greater than would otherwise be thought necessary.

The mathematical methods of crack stress analysis are capable of very high precision when used in conjunction with large digital computers. All the *K* calibrations which follow were obtained by such methods and are considered to be accurate, in themselves, to within at least 1 per cent (with the possible exception of the crack-notched round bar). The accuracy with which any of the *K* calibrations applies to a specific, detailed specimen design depends, however, on the compatability of the design with the mathematical model on which the *K* calibration is based.

Center-Cracked Plate Under Uniform Tension

The commonly used Irwin-Westergaard tangent relation for the finite-width center-cracked plate does not properly satisfy the boundary conditions for the specimen, as discussed in Ref *17*. Mathematical stress analyses of this case have been conducted recently by Forman and Kobayashi [*18*], by M. Isida (unpublished), and by Alexander Mendelson (also unpublished). The results of these studies are in excellent agreement with one another and can be expressed by a single curve as in Fig. 5—the individual results would not be distinguishable from the curve on the scale of this figure.

The results of Isida were used by the authors in a least-squares-best-fit procedure to obtain the following compact expression which fits the results to within 0.5 per cent over the range of $2a/W$ from 0 to 0.7

$$Y = K_I BW / Pa^{1/2} = 1.77 + 0.227(2a/W) - 0.510(2a/W)^2 + 2.7(2a/W)^3.$$

Over the range of $2a/W$ between 0 and 0.6 the following very simple expression is accurate to within 1 per cent

$$Y = 1.77(1 - 0.1(2a/W) + (2a/W)^2).$$

Polynomial expressions of K calibrations are particularly convenient for incorporation into data-reduction computer programs.

Figure 5 shows that the tangent expression gives K_I values that are lower than those given by the recent K calibration and that the difference increases with $2a/W$. It is generally agreed that the new calibration is more accurate, and it is recommended that it should be used in place of the tangent expression.

Double-Edge-Cracked Plate

The most accurate results for the double-edge-cracked plate are those obtained by Bowie [*17,18a*] using complex variable methods. The accuracy is probably within 1 per cent. These results are fitted by the following equation to within 1 per cent for values of $2a/W$ from 0 to 0.7.

$$Y = \frac{K_I BW}{Pa^{1/2}} = 1.98 + 0.36 \frac{2a}{W} - 2.12 \left(\frac{2a}{W}\right)^2 + 3.42 \left(\frac{2a}{W}\right)^3$$

Single-Edge-Cracked Plate Specimens

There are several forms of single-edge-cracked plate specimens for K_{Ic} testing, and these can be classified according to the manner in which they are loaded, for instance: pin-loading in tension (compact specimens that are extremely eccentrically loaded in tension are called crackline loaded specimens in this report); four-point bending; and three-point bending. Boundary collocation studies of all these variations have been reported [14–16,19], and the K calibrations will be discussed in turn.

Single-Edge-Cracked Plates in Tension

In an earlier report by the authors [10] the K calibration given was derived from experimental compliance measurements on specimens that were pin-loaded through the centerline [13]. It is now considered that the boundary collocation K calibration by Gross et al [14], since extended to cover a larger range of the relative crack length a/W, is more accurate. In this mathematical treatment it is assumed that the tensile load is uniformly distributed across the width of the specimen at a distance from the crack not less than the width. This assumption

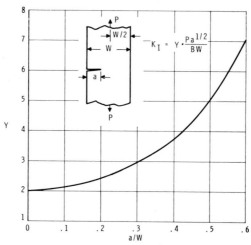

FIG. 6—*K calibration for single-edge-crack tension specimen.*

is consistent with pin-loading of the actual specimen if the distance between loading pin centers is not less than three times the specimen width.

The K calibration for uniform tension is represented by the following equation to within 0.4 per cent for all values of a/W up to 0.6

$$Y = K_I BW/Pa^{1/2} = 1.99 - 0.41(a/W) + 18.70(a/W)^2$$
$$- 38.48(a/W)^3 + 53.85(a/W)^4$$

A curve representing this relation is shown in Fig. 6. The earlier experimental results of Ref 13 are in agreement with Fig. 6 within 1 per cent in the range of a/W between 0.2 and 0.4 but deviate increasingly as a/W is increased beyond 0.4.

Calibrations for single-edge-cracked specimens that are eccentrically loaded in tension can be derived by superposition from the results for axial tension and pure bending, as discussed in Ref 15; however, such specimens appear to have considerably less practical interest than the more compact crackline specimens discussed later.

Single-Edge-Cracked Bend Specimens

Boundary collocation K calibrations for single-edge-cracked plate specimens in pure bending and in three-point bending are reported in Refs *15* and *16*, respectively, and have since been extended to cover

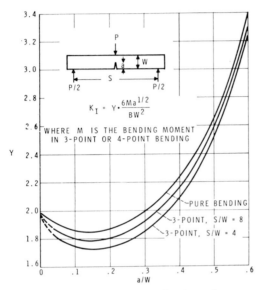

FIG. 7—*K calibrations for bend specimens.*

a larger range of a/W. Figure 7 shows curves representing the results for pure bending and for three-point bending with ratios of support span to specimen depth, S/W, of 4 and 8.

The K calibrations are represented by fourth-degree polynomials of the following form to within 0.2 per cent for all values of a/W up to 0.6

$$Y = K_I BW^2/6Ma^{1/2}$$

$$= A_0 + A_1(a/W) + A_2(a/W)^2 + A_3(a/W)^3 + A_4(a/W)^4$$

where M is the applied bending moment, and the coefficients A have the following values:

	A_0	A_1	A_2	A_3	A_4
Pure bending.......	+1.99	−2.47	+12.97	−23.17	+24.80
Three-point:					
$S/W = 8$........	+1.96	−2.75	+13.66	−23.98	+25.22
$S/W = 4$.	+1.93	−3.07	+14.53	−25.11	+25.80

It is considered that the K calibration for pure bending can be applied to four-point bending if the ratio of the minor span to specimen depth is not less than 2. If the ratio of the major, support span to specimen depth S/W is less than about 4, in either three-point or four-point bending, then it is difficult to avoid substantial errors from specimen indentation and friction at the supports. Even with ratios of S/W larger than 4 it is necessary to take precautions to minimize such errors, as discussed in a later section.

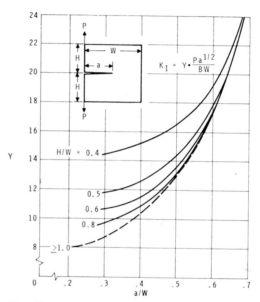

FIG. 8—*K calibrations for compact crackline loaded specimens.*

Crackline Loaded Single-Edge-Cracked Specimens

It appears that this type of specimen, defined earlier, can be made more compact than any other that could be used for K_{Ic} testing, and it is therefore of particular interest where economy of material or space for exposure of material (as in a nuclear reactor) is of prime importance. There are many possible design variations, and it is not yet clear what the optimum design should be. An early design, due to Manjoine [20], has been the subject of considerable study and development, including boundary collocation K calibration [21–23]. A somewhat different line of development has been pursued by Ripling [24], and Ripling's K calibration has been independently confirmed by boundary collocation analysis [19].

For illustrative purposes a set of K calibration curves for compact crackline loaded specimens are shown in Fig. 8. These are derived from unpublished work by Gross and show the effect of varying the relative specimen half-height H/W, as well as the relative crack length a/W. For $H/W = 0.444$ and $a/W = 0.38$, the specimen shown in Fig. 8 corresponds essentially to the original Manjoine design. On the basis of considerations regarding crack length and thickness given elsewhere in this report, and assuming a simple, two-pin method of loading the specimen, the present authors have tentatively concluded that a specimen with a/W and H/W each equal to about 0.6 would be close to optimum. Tests are scheduled to evaluate such a specimen design in the near future.

A further development due to Mostovoy [25] concerns the use of tapered crackline loaded specimens, in which the height varies with

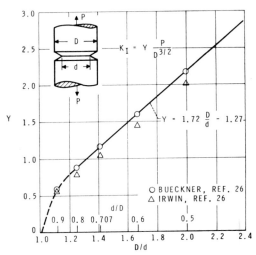

FIG. 9—*K calibration for circumferentially crack-notched round bar.*

distance from the loading line. By appropriate tapering, the K calibration relation can be made almost independent of a/W over a substantial range. This is experimentally convenient for fatigue crack propagation studies and might also have some advantage in K_{Ic} testing. There is clearly a great deal of further development to be expected in the application of crackline loaded specimens, and for this reason it would not be advisable to attempt to be more specific about their use at the present time.

Circumferentially Cracked Round Bar

A stress analysis for this type of specimen was conducted recently by Bueckner [26], who considers the accuracy of the resulting K calibration to be within 1 per cent (in the range of diameter ratio d/D between 0.5 and 0.9). Earlier K calibrations are not so accurate and differ considerably from Bueckner's, as shown in Table 8 of Ref *26*. It is generally agreed that Bueckner's results are the most accurate available, and it is recommended that they should be used.

Figure 9 shows Bueckner's results in the form of values of $Y = (K_I D^{3/2})/P$ plotted against D/d. This form was chosen because the relation between the two variables is represented within 1 per cent by the linear equation $Y = 1.72(D/d) - 1.27$, over the range of d/D between 0.5 and 0.8. If necessary, the linear fitting equation can be used to extrapolate Bueckner's results for values of d/D at least as low as 0.4. Such extrapolated values are consistent with Table 5 of Ref *17* and with the associated discussion given in that reference. For the purpose of comparison, Fig. 9 also shows the results ascribed to Irwin in Ref *26*, which are those that are most commonly used.

Specimen Size Requirements

Before proceeding with a discussion of specimen size requirements, it is appropriate to remind the reader of the assumptions inherent in the application of elastic fracture mechanics to engineering alloys and practical specimen types.

The accuracy with which K_{Ic} describes the fracture behavior of real materials depends on how well the stress intensity factor represents the conditions of stress and strain inside the fracture process zone. In this sense K_I gives an exact representation only in the limit of zero plastic strain. However, for many practical purposes a sufficient degree of accuracy may be obtained if the crack front plastic zone is small in comparison with the vicinity around the crack in which the stress intensity factor yields a satisfactory approximation of the exact elastic stress field.[2] The loss in accuracy associated with increasing the relative size of the plastic zone is gradual, and it is not possible at the present time to prescribe limits on the applicability of elastic fracture mechanics by means of theoretical considerations. Obviously, the question of what constitutes a satisfactory degree of accuracy will depend on the application, and in any case the useful limits of K_{Ic} testing in terms of specimen size requirements can only be established by suitable experiments.

In designing such experiments, it may be reasoned as follows: the region around the crack tip in which the elastic stresses are adequately described by a K analysis will increase with crack size and other pertinent specimen dimensions. Thus, the usefulness of K as a descriptive parameter regarding the fracture process should increase as the region of plastic strain at the crack front decreases in size compared with these dimensions. The region around the crack tip in which the elastic

---

[2] A detailed discussion of this point by Liu in Ref *27* is recommended for additional reading.

stresses will be adequately described by K will vary with the specimen geometry. For this reason and because the crack front plastic zone is complex in shape, it is unlikely that any single parameter can be used to accurately establish the minimum specimen size required for a K_{Ic} determination of a particular alloy. However, as discussed in a previous section of this report, it is appropriate to assume that $(K_{Ic}/\sigma_{YS})^2$ is a characteristic dimension of the plastic zone that should be useful in estimating specimen dimensions. The pertinent dimensions of plate specimens for K_{Ic} testing are crack length, thickness, and ligament (uncracked) length. It is assumed that a necessary condition for a K_{Ic} test to be valid is that each of these dimensions should exceed a certain multiple of $(K_{Ic}/\sigma_{YS})^2$, these multiples to be determined by an adequate number of trial K_{Ic} tests. By means of such tests, it should be possible to establish practically useful "working limits" for specimen dimensions. The lower limits of these dimensions for which K_{Ic} remains constant can then be expressed in terms of $(K_{Ic}/\sigma_{YS})^2$.

Since the above approach is different from that used previously in determining specimen size requirements, it is advisable to briefly review the past recommendations as summarized in the 5th Fracture Committee Report [5] and in a paper by the present authors [10]. Requirements on the specimen thickness B were formulated by Boyle et al [8] in terms of the plane stress plastic zone correction term $r_y = 1/\pi \cdot (K_{Ic}/\sigma_{YS})^2$, and it was suggested that B/r_y should be at least 4 in order that a distinct popin could be observed. This requirement was based on information derived from tests on sharply notched 7075-T6 aluminum alloy specimens, before the substantial effect of crack sharpness on the measured plane strain fracture toughness had been appreciated (see "Specimen Preparation and Testing"). While the work of Boyle et al is helpful as a guide in formulating further experiments, the use of data from notched specimens without cracks to establish specimen size requirements is misleading.

Hitherto, requirements on the crack length and ligament size have not been stated directly. Instead, it has been assumed that a specimen would be of sufficient size if the ratio of net or nominal stress to the yield strength did not exceed some particular value. For symmetrically loaded plate tensile specimens it may be inferred from the 5th Fracture Committee Report that the net stress should be less than 80 per cent of the yield strength[3] for a valid K_{Ic} test [5]. In the case of single-edge-cracked tension and bend specimens, the present authors assumed previously that the nominal stress at the crack tip should be less than the yield

---

[3] In this connection it should be noted that the limitation of the net stress in terms of the yield strength given in this report was derived from tests on thin, center-slotted panels of tough alloys (K_c tests). The crack lengths at fracture instability, and therefore the K_c values, were very difficult to determine accurately (see Ref 28).

TABLE 1—Composition of maraging steel used in the NASA-NRL cooperative program.[a]

Supplier	Heat Number	Heat Treatment	σ_{YS}, ksi	Composition									
				C	Ni	Co	Mo	Ti	Al	Mn	Si	P	S
Republic............	3920913 ½-in. plate	1600 F, 1 hr, AC + 850 F, 3 hr	242	0.020	18.20	8.60	4.70	0.70	0.09	0.06	0.06	0.005	0.002
Republic............	3930641 1-in. plate	age 900 F, 3 hr	259	0.020	18.35	7.18	5.32	0.32	0.04	0.05	0.09	0.006	0.005
Allegheny-Ludlum	24349 1-in. plate	age 900 F, 3 hr	285	0.030	18.53	8.89	4.64	0.69	0.15	0.021	0.06	0.003	0.010

[a] All steels were consumable electrode vacuum melted.

strength [10]. These limiting stress ratios were then used in conjunction with the appropriate K calibrations to calculate an optimum value of crack length to specimen width and also to derive K_{Ic} measurement capacities for various specimen types [10]. This procedure resulted in optimum ratios of crack length to width that were different for different specimen types and which now appear to be too low.

It appears that basing specimen design requirements on a particular value of the ratio of the net or nominal stress to yield strength is open to the following objections. First, the so-called nominal stress is an arbi-

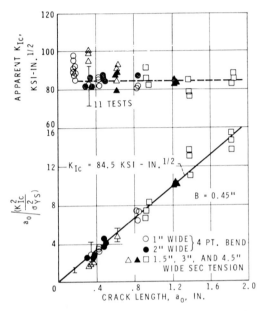

FIG. 10—*Effect of crack length on apparent K_{Ic} for single-edge-cracked tension and bend tests on 242 yield strength maraging steel.*

trary quantity and is defined differently for different types of specimens. Also, the use of the nominal stress criterion leads to a ratio of required crack length to plastic zone size which decreases with decreasing ratio of crack length to specimen width. This is inconsistent with the rationale of linear elastic fracture mechanics.

What follows will illustrate how the problem of specimen design may be approached through suitable experiments designed to establish the required limits on the ratios between the three pertinent plate specimen dimensions and $(K_{Ic}/\sigma_{YS})^2$. A necessary requirement of this approach is that the "true" mean K_{Ic} of the material must be accurately established by testing specimens of sufficient crack length, thickness, and ligament size. Once the true mean K_{Ic} is established in this way, a systematic series of trial K_{Ic} tests is made to determine how far a given dimension may be reduced without significant change in the K_{Ic} values obtained. Tests of this type are time consuming and expensive, but no other satisfactory procedure is evident at this time. The experiments to be described are confined to tests on three heats of maraging steel (see Table 1) used for the NASA-NRL cooperative program. The limited information so far available from this program is indicative but not conclusive regarding specimen size requirements.

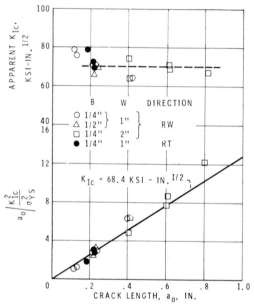

FIG. 11—*Effect of crack length on apparent K_{Ic} for 4-point bend tests on 259 ksi yield strength maraging steel.*

Crack Length Requirement

The effect of crack length on the apparent K_{Ic} is shown in Fig. 10 for single-edge-crack bend and tension specimens of 0.45-in. thick, 242 ksi yield strength maraging steel, cracked in the *WR* direction.[4] The bend specimens were either 1 or 2 in. wide, and the single-edge-crack tension specimens were 1.5, 3, or 4.5 in. wide. All specimens exhibited load-displacement curves with negligible nonlinearity and fractured completely at popin. Except for the shortest crack lengths, it is apparent that there is no trend of K_{Ic} with crack length. The grand average of all 0.45-in.-thick specimens is 86.2 ksi·(in.)[1/2]. It can be shown[5] that the average

---

[4] For nomenclature concerning the direction of crack propagation, see Ref 2, p. 391.

[5] The statistical test used was based on the ratio of the difference in averages to the range for the sample (see Ref 29, Section 2.2.1).

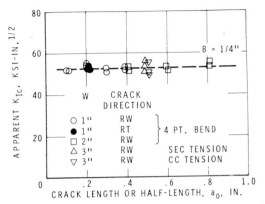

FIG. 12—*Effect of crack length on apparent K_{Ic} for 285 ksi yield strength maraging steel tested using several specimen types.*

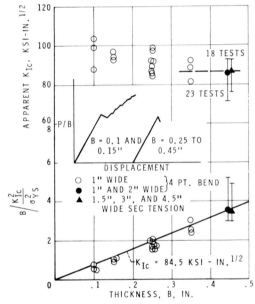

FIG. 13—*Effect of thickness on apparent K_{Ic} for 242 ksi yield strength maraging steel tested using bend and single-edge-crack tension specimens.*

K_{Ic} (90.8 ksi·(in.)$^{1/2}$) for the group of bend specimens having crack lengths of about 0.17 in. is significantly higher than the grand average. The tension specimens with the shortest crack lengths also had an average K_{Ic} (98.2 ksi·(in.)$^{1/2}$) significantly higher than the grand average. The average K_{Ic} for all other crack lengths was 84.5 ksi·(in.)$^{1/2}$, and this is considered to be the true value. As can be seen from Fig. 10, the value of $a_0/(K_{Ic}/\sigma_{YS})^2$ is less than 2 for crack lengths of 0.17 in. and about 2.5 for crack lengths of 0.32 in.

Additional information concerning the influence of crack length may be obtained from a series of bend tests made on 259 ksi yield strength maraging steel (Fig. 11). Specimens $\frac{1}{4}$ and $\frac{1}{2}$ in. thick, having a wide range of crack lengths, were cut from a single 1-in.-thick plate of this steel. Load versus electric potential records exhibited distinct popin indications for all crack lengths investigated. While the data from these tests are very limited, it does indicate that the apparent K_{Ic} value increases at $a_0/(K_{Ic}/\sigma_{YS})^2$ ratios less than about 2.5.

Further data regarding the influence of crack length are shown in Fig. 12 for a 285 ksi yield strength maraging steel. Various types of

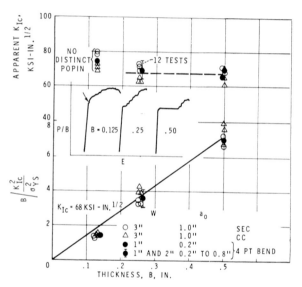

FIG. 14—*Effect of thickness on popin behavior and apparent K_{Ic} for 259 ksi yield strength maraging steel tested using several specimen types.*

$\frac{1}{4}$-in.-thick specimens were machined from a single 1-in.-thick plate of this steel. Load-potential records showed distinct popin indication for all crack lengths, and within the scatter no trend of K_{Ic} with crack length is noted. The shortest crack length specimens of this series had a ratio of $a_0/(K_{Ic}/\sigma_{YS})^2$ of about 3.8. A ratio of 2.5 would correspond to a crack length of about 0.085 in.

The results discussed above indicate that the apparent K_{Ic} may overestimate the true value if the crack length is less than some limit which may depend on the material. For the steels investigated, this limit appears to correspond to a ratio of $a_0/(K_{Ic}/\sigma_{YS})^2$ of about 2.5. However, it should be emphasized that additional data on other types of alloys are necessary to set a firm lower limit on this ratio.

Thickness Requirement

The influence of specimen thickness is illustrated in Fig. 13 for the 242 ksi yield strength maraging steel. The group of 18 single-edge-crack specimens and the group of 23 bend specimens, both 0.45 in. thick, represent all data from Fig. 10 having sufficient crack length. The 1-in.-wide bend specimens with thicknesses from 0.1 to 0.35 in. were machined from the broken halves of the 0.45-in.-thick tension specimens. The two smallest thicknesses, 0.1 and 0.15 in., yielded load-displacement records having well defined popin steps preceded by negligible deviation from linearity. The bend specimens at 0.25 and 0.35-in. thickness ruptured completely at popin. Using the same statistical procedure as employed in analysis of the crack length data, the K_{Ic} for each group of

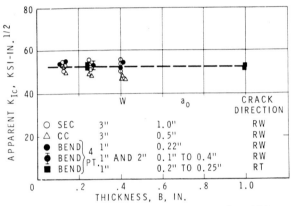

FIG. 15—*Effect of thickness on apparent K_{Ic} for 285 ksi yield strength maraging steel tested using several specimen types.*

smaller thicknesses was tested to determine whether it was significantly greater than the average for the 0.45-in.-thick specimens. The differences were significant at the 5 per cent level for thicknesses 0.25 in. and lower, but not for a thickness of 0.35 in. On the basis of this analysis it is concluded that specimens of this material thinner than 0.35 in. are likely to give significantly higher K_{Ic} values than thicker specimens. This thickness partition corresponds to a ratio of $B/(K_{Ic}/\sigma_{YS})^2$ of about 2.5.

Additional data illustrating the thickness effect are shown in Fig. 14 for 259 ksi yield strength maraging steel. Single-edge-cracked and center-cracked tension specimens and bend specimens of three thicknesses were machined from a single 1-in.-thick plate. Two widths and several crack lengths were investigated for the bend specimens, while a single size was used for the tension specimens. All specimens were cracked in the *RW* direction. Electric potential measurements were made during the course of these tests, and typical load-potential records are shown in the insets of Fig. 14. The effect of reducing the specimen thickness was to produce load-potential records which were more difficult to interpret, and tests at $\frac{1}{8}$-in. thickness gave records which exhibited no clear popin indication. Attempts to select popin loads from these records on the basis of deviations from linearity (indicated by arrow in Fig. 14) gave K_{Ic} values which significantly exceeded the average established by tests at the two larger thicknesses. These data also suggest that a ratio of $B/(K_{Ic}/\sigma_{YS})^2$ somewhere between 2 and 3 is necessary for valid K_{Ic} determination. Similar tests on 7075-T6 aluminum alloy gave essentially the same result.

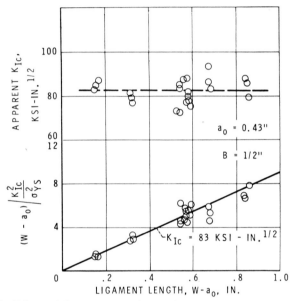

FIG. 16—*Effect of ligament length on the apparent K_{Ic} for 242 ksi yield strength maraging steel tested in 4-point bending.*

Further data for maraging steel at a yield strength level of 285 ksi are shown in Fig. 15. Specimens of various types covering a wide range of thickness were machined from a single 1-in.-thick plate and cracked in the *RW* or *RT* direction. Well defined popin indications on load-potential records were obtained at all thicknesses investigated, and within the scatter no trend of K_{Ic} with thickness is noted. The thinnest specimens of this series had a $B/(K_{Ic}/\sigma_{YS})^2$ of about 3.5. A ratio of 2.5 would correspond to a thickness of 0.090 in.

The data reported here regarding the effect of thickness indicate that the apparent K_{Ic} value may increase below a certain limiting thickness even though distinct popin indications are obtained. In other cases the effect of reducing the thickness is to render the popin indication so indistinct as to make unambiguous interpretation of the record extremely difficult. A limiting value of $B/(K_{Ic}/\sigma_{YS})^2$ for a valid K_{Ic} test on the alloys investigated appears to be about 2.5. However, it should be emphasized that the limiting value of this ratio may vary from alloy to alloy, and further tests of this type are needed to establish a conservative lower limit.

Ligament Requirement

In order to investigate the effect of ligament length $(W - a_0)$, a series of bend tests was made for 242 ksi yield strength, maraging steel specimens having a constant crack length but varying width, as shown in Fig. 16. The crack length selected (0.43 in.) for this series of tests was adequate for a valid K_{Ic} determination, as can be seen from Fig. 10. All specimens ruptured completely at popin, and within the scatter of the data there is no trend of K_{Ic} with $(W - a_0)$. The results do not clearly define an upper limit on $(W - a_0)$, but examination of the load-displacement records for this series of tests showed that the deviation from linearity preceding rupture was very small for all specimens except those having the smallest ligament. The deviations from linearity for the latter specimens were distinctly greater, which would tend to indicate that the limiting ligament length is not much less than the smallest value investigated. While more information of this type is certainly needed, the data do indicate that higher a_0/W values can be used than were previously suggested.

Summary of Suggested Size Requirements

On the basis of the information presented it is suggested that both the crack length and thickness should be greater than some multiple of $(K_{Ic}/\sigma_{YS})^2$ for a valid K_{Ic} test. The data available so far indicate that this multiple should not be less than about 2.5. This value, however, should be regarded as a preliminary estimate pending development of adequate data on a variety of alloys. Apparently the ligament length can be somewhat smaller than the crack length; however, ratios of crack length to width greater than about 0.5 are undesirable because the K calibration curve for single-edge-cracked tension and bend tests (see Figs. 6 and 7) rises very steeply at the high a/W values. Under these circumstances small errors in measured crack length can have undesirable large effects on the calculated K_{Ic}-values.

Specimen dimensions consistent with the requirement that neither a nor B should be less than 2.5 $(K_{Ic}/\sigma_{YS})^2$ are considerably greater than hitherto considered necessary [5, 8, 10]. For example, a crack-notch bend specimen about 2 in. thick and 4 in. deep would be required for a material having a K_{Ic} of 160 ksi·(in.)$^{1/2}$ and a yield strength of 180 ksi. The specimen dimensions for lower strength materials of high toughness, such as HY-80 steel, would probably be quite impractical. However, under some circumstances, K_{Ic} testing is useful for evaluation of lower strength materials. There are widely used structural materials with yield strengths below 100 ksi having K_{Ic} values sufficiently low that plane strain fracture toughness measurements can be made with specimens of practical sizes. Furthermore, if a sufficiently large specimen is used that is designed to "match" the expected applications, the fact that the speci-

TABLE 2—*Variability of valid[a] K_{Ic} results.*

Material	Heat Treatment	Yield Strength, ksi	K_{Ic} Tests			
			Number of Tests, n	Mean K_{Ic}, $\bar{X}$, ksi·(in.)$^{1/2}$	Standard Deviation, S, ksi·(in.)$^{1/2}$	$S/\bar{X}$
Maraging steel (300)..	900 F, 3 hr	285	38	51.75	2.47	0.0478
Maraging steel (250)..	900 F, 3 hr	259	23	68.4	3.51	0.0515
Maraging steel (300)..	850 F, 3 hr	242	44	84.5	4.67	0.0555
Aluminum 7075 (½-in. thick).............	T651	79	24	26.8	1.32	0.0495

[a] Valid according to the tentative criteria suggested in this report.

TABLE 3—*Recommended minimum specimen dimensions and ratios of required load to yield strength for $(K_{Ic}/\sigma_{YS})^2 = 1$.*

(For other values of $(K_{Ic}/\sigma_{YS})^2$, the dimensions should be in proportion to this factor, and the loads in proportion to its square.)

Specimen Type	Thickness, in.	Crack Length, in.	Width or Diameter, in.	Specimen Length, in.	Load/σ_{YS}, in.^{2}
Crack-notched round bar.....	...	2.5 ($D/2$-$d/2$)	10 (D)	40	14.7
Center-crack plate............	2.5	5.0 (2a)	10	40	7.5
Double-edge-crack plate......	2.5	2.5	10	40	7.9
Single-edge-crack plate, tension......................	2.5	2.5	5	20	1.6
Single-edge-crack plate, 4-point bend (8:1::span:depth) (2:1::minor span:depth)....	2.5	2.5	5	41	0.33
Single-edge crack plate, 3-point bend (4:1::span: depth).....................	2.5	2.5	5	21	0.50
Crackline loaded plate........	2.5	...	...	...	...

men is not large enough to provide an acceptable K_{Ic} value may be an assurance that the material is tough enough for the application. The word "match" is used here in the sense that the specimen has a thickness appropriate to the application and a crack length consistent with inspection capability, reliability, and service circumstances.

Variability of K_{Ic} Results

It was pointed out in the "Introduction" that the plane strain crack toughness of a given sample of material is characterized by the distribution of K_{Ic} values determined on specimens taken from the sample. The data obtained on the NASA-NRL cooperative program and presented in Figs. 10 through 16 for three heats of maraging steel are sufficient to permit a judgment concerning the variability of K_{Ic} results. A statistical analysis of the maraging steel data, shown in Table 2, gives the mean value $\overline{X}$, standard deviation, S, the coefficient of variation $S/\overline{X}$ for all valid K_{Ic} information. Added to this table are some results obtained on $\frac{1}{2}$-in.-thick 7075-T651 aluminum alloy plate.

It will be noted that the coefficients of variation did not differ significantly among the various alloy conditions tested and are within the range that might be expected for a mechanical property relating to the fracture of metallic alloys. For example, a statistical analysis of impact

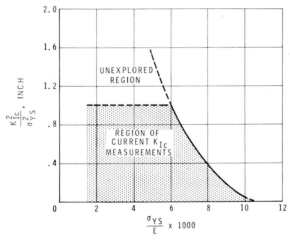

FIG. 17—*Boundaries of the region of current plane strain crack toughness tests (based on data for steels).*

data obtained by Driscoll for SAE 4340 [*30*] was given in Ref 3. This analysis showed a coefficient of variation of 0.041 and 0.044 for tests on two types of impact machines. These values are not considered to be significantly different from those given for the coefficient of variation of K_{Ic} in Table 2.

Practical Specimen Types

This section deals with specific recommendations regarding the dimensions of the various types of K_{Ic} test specimens, their load requirements, and various other considerations that enter into the choice of a specimen type for a particular application. Detailed drawings of the various types of specimens are given in Appendix II. In addition, this section includes some comments on the use of surface crack specimens and precracked Charpy specimens.

Recommended Specimen Dimensions and Corresponding Load Requirements

Table 3 is a summary of recommended minimum specimen dimensions for six different types of plate specimens and for the crack-notched round bar, based on the discussion in the preceding section. For consistency it is assumed that the depth of the annular crack-notch in the round bar, $(D - d)/2$, is equivalent to the crack length in the edge-crack plate specimens and therefore equal to $2.5(K_{Ic}/\sigma_{YS})^2$. The ratio of total crack length to specimen width in the plate specimens, and the ratio d/D in the round bar, is taken as 0.5.[6] This choice is a compromise between the desire to extend the K_{Ic} measurement limit for a given specimen as far as possible, and the recognition that the K_{Ic} measurement accuracy deteriorates with increasing relative crack length. The last column in the table gives the ratios of required load to yield strength corresponding to the dimensions listed, assuming that the characteristic material dimensions $(K_{Ic}/\sigma_{YS})^2$ is equal to 1 in. For other values of this characteristic material dimension, the specimen dimensions would be proportional to $(K_{Ic}/\sigma_{YS})^2$, and the required load proportional to $(K_{Ic}/\sigma_{YS})^4$.

To determine suitable specimen dimensions for an unfamiliar material it is first necessary to decide the highest level of $(K_{Ic}/\sigma_{YS})^2$ that the material is likely to exhibit. Figure 17 is provided to help the reader in this respect. In this figure the lower part of the curve which bounds the "Region of Current K_{Ic} Measurements" is based on the highest values of K_{Ic} that have been measured for steels with yield strengths between 180,000 and 300,000 psi. The horizontal dashed line represents the highest level of $(K_{Ic}/\sigma_{YS})^2$ that has been reached to date. The figure shows $(K_{Ic}/\sigma_{YS})^2$ versus the ratio of yield strength to Young's modulus, σ_{YS}/E, so that nonferrous alloys could be plotted for comparison. There is insufficient information to provide upper-bound curves for nonferrous alloys, but all nonferrous alloy results known to the authors lie well below the bounding curve for steels. It is recommended that specimen dimensions for unfamiliar materials should be based on values of $(K_{Ic}/\sigma_{YS})^2$ taken from the bounding curve in Fig. 17 whenever the dimensions of the available material stock permit. These specimen dimensions will usually be more than adequate. If it is necessary to use smaller dimensions, then the adequacy of the dimensions can only be decided after the tests have been conducted.

---

[6] Previous practice has been to use a d/D of 0.707 for the notched round bar on the basis that this gives the highest K for a given notch (net area) stress. The authors assume that additional K_{Ic} measurement capacity can be gained with negligible loss in accuracy by using a $d/D = 0.5$. However, it should be noted that no experiments have been performed to check the validity of this assumption.

Considerations in Selecting Specimens for Particular Applications

On the basis of the foregoing recommendations concerning specimen dimensions and load requirements, it would appear that bend (or possibly crackline loaded specimens) would be the only ones of interest for K_{Ic} determination. However, under some circumstances other considerations than "efficiency" can determine the selection of a particular specimen type or crack length to width ratio.

Bend specimens certainly do have a wide range of application and are suited to testing plates or forgings, because directionality effects can readily be investigated by suitable orientation of the specimen with respect to the fiber. Tests in the short transverse direction frequently present difficulties due to the limited thickness available; however, in some cases extension pieces can be welded to the test section. If the tests must be conducted in a limited lateral space, such as might be encountered in reactor tubes or a cryostat, the single-edge-crack tension specimen offers the advantage of requiring a minimum amount of space normal to the loading direction. It should be noted that single-edge-crack tension specimens shorter than those recommended here have been used by some investigators [31]. The K calibrations given in this report are not applicable to such short specimens because of interaction between the stress fields of the loading holes and that of the crack. This interaction makes an analytical stress analysis extremely difficult, and K calibrations for short specimens must be determined by experimental compliance measurements which are in themselves subject to several uncertainties (see Section on "K Calibrations of Specimens").

The center-cracked and double-edge-cracked plate specimens are of considerable interest from a theoretical standpoint since they are loaded in pure tension and provide a baseline for the development of other specimen types. Their high load and material requirements exclude them from consideration in most practical applications of K_{Ic} testing. However, they do provide a means for (1) determining crack extension resistance curves as discussed previously by the present authors [10] and (2) investigating the fracture mode transition in terms of the notch strength as a function of thickness change.

While a crack length to width ratio of 0.5 has been recommended for the plate specimens listed in Table 3, there is no reason why smaller values could not be used in special circumstances provided there is adequate crack length. For example, in testing weldments it is frequently desirable to locate the tip of the crack in some particular region of the metal structure and to relate the popin load to the K_{Ic} value of this region.

The circumferentially cracked round bar has received considerable attention in the past as a specimen for use in studying the influence of notch sharpness. In investigations of this type it has the advantage that notches of a particular contour may be produced to close tolerances by cylindrical grinding or lathe turning. As described in the 4th Fracture Committee Report [4], this specimen, provided with a very sharp notch, may be used to screen alloys regarding their fracture behavior in thick sections. However, aside from its high load and material requirement, the cracked round bar is not well suited for K_{Ic} testing unless the particular application dictates the use of this type of specimen (for example, an investigation of the effects of cracks at the base of screw threads). While machined circumferential notches are relatively easy to produce to close tolerances in the notch, round specimen fatigue cracking is difficult to control so that the crack front is concentric with the loading axis. In addition, special precautions are necessary to reduce eccentricity of loading during testing in order to avoid undesirable scatter. In the absence of eccentricity the fracture properties of this specimen will be largely controlled by the region on the crack circumference having the lowest toughness. The fact that a cracked round bar fractures without shear lips is sometimes taken to mean that the specimen may be used to determine K_{Ic} values at much higher ratios of K_{Ic}/σ_{YS} than would be possible using plate specimens. This, of course, is not true since the absence of shear lips does not ensure the absence of extensive plastic deformation in this or any other specimen.

Surface-Crack Specimen

The surface-crack specimen was developed originally for the purpose of simulating flaws of the type which are frequently encountered in service [32,33]. Photographs of several such service fractures are shown in Ref 6. Subject to the conditions which apply to all K_{Ic} test specimens, measurements of K_{Ic} can be made with surface-crack specimens, but they are not limited to this purpose. Tests of surface-crack specimens provide direct information on the effects of realistic flaws on fracture strength in circumstances which are not amenable to a plane strain fracture mechanics analysis, for instance, where the applied boundary stress exceeds the tensile yield strength. In addition, they have been found to be very useful in the evaluation of subcritical plane strain flaw growth [33a,33b]. The analysis required to obtain stress intensity factors for the surface-crack specimen is much more complex (and consequently less well understood) than for the previously discussed through-cracked plate specimens. Also, the surface-crack specimen is not as efficient in terms of specimen size and load requirements as the through-cracked plate specimens. For these reasons, it is considered less suitable for general K_{Ic} testing. However, in some circumstances it may be both necessary and desirable to use this specimen. For example, in performing a failure analysis of a hardware component which failed as result of a surface crack, it is desirable to evaluate the fracture resistance of the component material with a precracked specimen which simulates the actual hardware fracture origin.

The conventional expression for the stress intensity factor for this specimen is an approximate solution derived by Irwin [33c] for a semi-elliptical surface crack in an infinite solid. Consequently, the expression is not directly applicable when the flaw is very deep with respect to the specimen thickness (that is, greater than approximately one half the thickness) or very long with respect to the specimen width, and, of

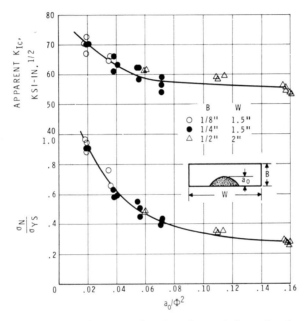

FIG. 18—*Effect of crack size on the K_{Ic} value and the ratio of net-stress-to-yield-strength for 285 ksi yield strength maraging steel using surface cracked specimens.*

course, when the applied boundary stress approaches and exceeds the material tensile yield strength. The determination of specimen size requirements for the surface-crack specimen is a difficult task. Likewise, it is a difficult task to predict the performance of actual hardware components containing surface (and internal) cracks which are not always small with respect to the material thickness. Theoretical and experimental work is badly needed to evaluate the effects of free boundaries and combined stress fields on the performance of both surface-crack specimens and actual hardware containing such cracks. Some noteworthy contributions to date include the approximate analysis of deep surface flaws by Kobayashi [36], the analysis of large internal flaws and coplanar internal flaws by Kobayashi et al [35], and the analysis of the semicircular surface flaws subjected to thermal stress and bending stress by Smith [35a].

There are only limited data available which permit the comparison of fracture toughness values determined using surface crack specimens with those obtained from a variety of other specimen types. Some information of this nature available from the NASA-NRL cooperative program is illustrated in Fig. 18, which shows the effect of crack size for surface-crack specimens of 285 ksi yield strength maraging steel, aged before fatigue cracking (see Table 1). Electrical potential and acoustic instrumentation was used on all specimens. These measurements indicated no stable crack extension at crack sizes[7] greater than $a/\phi^2 = 0.02$, and only very small amounts of crack extension preceding maximum load at this crack size. As discussed in the last section of this report, a large number of tests on this same plate using a variety of other specimen types gave an average K_{Ic} level of 52 ksi$\cdot$(in.)$^{1/2}$, independent of whether the cracks were propagating in the same direction as those in the surface crack specimens or into the edges of the plate. The level of K_{Ic} for the surface-crack specimens closely approaches 52 ksi$\cdot$(in.)$^{1/2}$ for a/ϕ^2 ratios above about 0.06. Specimens having a/ϕ^2 values smaller than 0.06 have crack depths less than $a = 0.09 = 2.5 \, (K_{Ic}/\sigma_{YS})^2$. These results illustrate that apparent K_{Ic} values determined using specimens with small cracks can be too high for some materials. The implication is that the strength of a specimen containing a small flaw could be underestimated by calculations based on the K_{Ic} values obtained from specimens containing larger cracks. Of even more importance is that one might overestimate the strength of a hardware component containing a large flaw if the calculation were based upon apparent K_{Ic} values obtained from specimens containing small flaws. This trend of apparent decreasing K_{Ic} values with increasing flaw size (decreasing stress level) for some materials and test temperatures has also been noted by Randall [34] for D6a steel and by Tiffany et al [33b] for 5Al-2.5Sn-Ti tested at -423 F. These references also contain data where this trend is not readily apparent.

The reason for this inconsistency in behavior of the surface crack specimen is presently not understood. However, in some cases the decrease in apparent K_{Ic} with increasing flaw size may be related to formation of small splits or delaminations at the crack tip which would be more pronounced for specimens failing at the higher stress levels. These splits could cause the crack to become unstable at a location on its periphery other than at the point of maximum depth as is assumed to be the case in the customary analysis. In any case, it is apparent that when surface-crack specimens are used to determine K_{Ic} values it is desirable to test several different crack sizes to insure that the minimum possible K_{Ic} value is determined.

---

[7] Where ϕ^2 is a crack shape parameter as discussed in Ref 2.

While Refs 5 and 10 made some recommendations regarding the size requirements for surface crack specimens, it now appears that these requirements are inadequate for some materials. It is clear that much additional development is needed and hopefully will be forthcoming so that final requirements can be specified with a high degree of confidence.

Cracked Charpy Specimens

Impact tests of cracked Charpy specimens are frequently employed for screening alloys regarding the effect of metallurgical variables on relative toughness level (for example, Refs 37 and 38). In this case the pendulum energy loss divided by the initial uncracked area (W/A) is reported. Some investigations have converted the W/A values directly to $\mathcal{G}_{Ic}$ (or K_{Ic}) or have tested the specimen in slow bending, treating it much the same as a conventional single-edge-crack bend test.

The limitations inherent in the use of cracked Charpy specimens for K_{Ic} measurement have been discussed previously in detail [10] and will only be briefly reviewed here. The basic limitation is, of course, the specimen size. It should be evident from the preceding discussion of size requirements for bend specimens that the cracked Charpy specimen with a width of 0.394 in. and an $a/W = 0.5$ has a maximum K_{Ic} measurement capacity of only 0.28 σ_{YS}, whether tested in impact or slow bending. If tested in impact the conversion of pendulum energy loss to $\mathcal{G}_{Ic}$ involves at least three assumptions: (1) all of the energy loss has been converted to fracture energy, (2) the fracture mode corresponds to plane strain conditions throughout the entire specimen cross section, and (3) the integrated fracture work divided by the fracture area is equal to $\mathcal{G}_{Ic}$, implying no appreciable dependence of $\mathcal{G}_{Ic}$ on crack speed. It is possible to develop procedures to identify and correct for extraneous energy losses. However, for the second assumption to be true requires the testing of sufficiently large specimens to suppress the formation of side boundary plastic regions[8] which would relax the transverse constraint responsible for the plane strain conditions at the crack front. This requirement would correspond to testing bend specimens of sufficient size that complete fracture occurs at popin, a condition that can be met in Charpy specimen sizes only for very brittle alloys. The use of W/A values for screening alloys regarding their relative K_{Ic} levels is an uncertain procedure if the impact specimen fractures under mixed mode conditions, unless it can be shown that the mixed mode fracture energies and the plane strain frac-

---

[8] Attempts have been made to suppress the development of these plastic regions by the use of specimens containing brittle boundaries. While this technique may be useful in some cases, it can lead to additional complexities. The possible difficulties associated with suppression of side boundary deformation either by use of face grooves or brittle boundaries are discussed in the section on "Specimen Preparation and Testing."

ture energies bear the same relation among the alloy conditions investigated.

Instrumentation

The types and basic principles of instrumentation suitable for detecting crack extension in fracture toughness tests have been reviewed previously [10]. For plane strain toughness testing, methods involving the measurement of displacements, electrical potential, and acoustic emission are most suitable. Recent developments concerning these three techniques are described in this section. In addition, calibration curves are presented which permit estimation of the crack extension from records of load

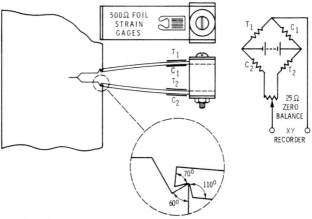

FIG. 19—*Double cantilever beam gage and method of mounting on crack-notched specimen for displacement measurement (designed by J. E. Srawley).*

versus displacement or load versus potential change. These calibrations are useful in analysis of popin indications.

Displacement Measurements

The relative displacement referred to here is measured between points on either side of the end of the notch in edge-cracked specimens, and across the center slot at the specimen centerline in center-cracked specimens. Various types of transducers have been used to make these measurements [10]. A most satisfactory method employs electric resistance strain gages mounted on a suitably designed flexural element which deforms elastically as the crack notch or slot opens. Krafft [39,40] has described the use of gages of this type in displacement measurements on center-crack and single-edge-crack specimens. He prefers a bi-lobed clip gage [40] to measure displacements in a low-temperature bath and at high strain rates. In general, considerable effort is required to develop gages of a particular type, and care must be taken to insure that adequate sensitivity is combined with a high degree of linearity of output with respect to displacements at the measuring points. Linearity of gage output is essential if ambiguity in interpretation of test records is to be avoided. A particularly troublesome problem affecting the linearity is maintenance of registery at the measuring points, and any satisfactory design should provide for positive positioning during the entire course of a test.

A simple double cantilever beam gage has been developed by Fisher et al [41] which appears quite suitable for general K_{Ic} testing and combines high sensitivity with linearity of output. The flexures are cantilever

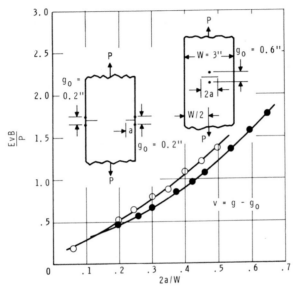

FIG. 20—*Calibration curves for converting displacement measurements to crack lengths for center- and double-edge-crack specimens.*

arms arranged in the design shown in Fig. 19. These arms are made from solution-treated beta titanium, which has a high ratio of yield strength to modulus. Epoxy resin bonded foil resistance strain gages are fixed to either side of each arm and connected in the bridge arrangement shown. Grooves in the ends of the cantilevers contact knife edges which are machined into edge-cracked specimens on either side of the crack slot. For center-cracked specimens it has been found satisfactory to attach small knife edges by means of screws to the specimen surface at the centerline on either side of the crack slot. This method of locating the gage has proved very satisfactory in that the gage is positively positioned during the entire test and yet released without damage when the specimen ruptures. However, precision machining of the grooves in the beams and knife edges in the specimen is essential for satisfactory operation of the gage. When calibrated by a supermicrometer, this gage is linear within 0.0001 in. over the range of 0.200 to 0.250 in. The sensitivity is about 37.5 mv/v/in., giving a magnification factor of about 750 for an X-Y recorder sensitivity of 0.5 mv/in. and a bridge excitation of 10 v. Conventional resistance strain gage power supplies and wiring techniques may be employed. By use of a commercially available converter, the

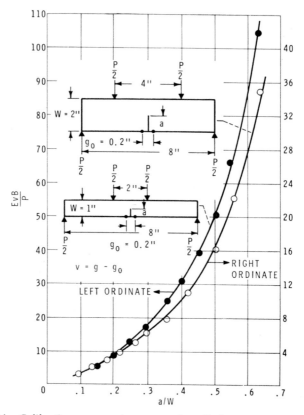

FIG. 21—*Calibration curves for converting displacement measurements to crack lengths for bend specimens.*

output of the strain gage bridge may be used to drive the strain axis of the stress-strain recorder of a testing machine.

Calibration curves relating the displacements to relative crack extension are shown in Figs. 20 to 22 for several commonly used fracture toughness specimens. These plots give the dimensionless quantity vEB/P as a function of the ratio of crack length to specimen width. The symbols are defined on the graphs. These calibration curves were obtained using the gage lengths indicated in Figs. 20 to 22, and apply to any specimen having the same geometric proportions as the calibration specimens.

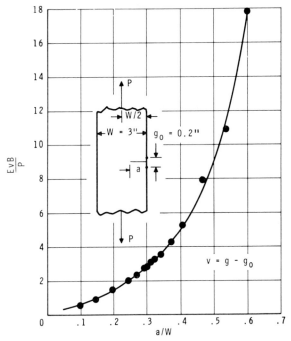

FIG. 22—*Calibration curve for converting displacement measurements to crack length single-edge-crack tension specimens.*

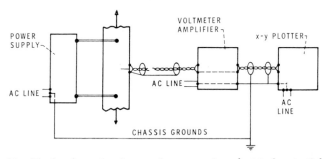

FIG. 23—*Block schematic of setup for measuring electrical potential showing arrangement of shields and grounds.*

Strictly speaking, the gage length should also be proportioned; however, its value is not critical provided the length is less than the crack length.

Electric Potential Measurement

The necessary equipment is illustrated in Fig. 23, which gives a block schematic of the setup. Experience with this method in tests at room temperature over the past two years has revealed a source of difficulty in the pickup of interfering signals which produce spurious responses of the *X-Y* recorder. The voltmeter-amplifier has an inherently high rejection for frequencies of 60 cps and above combined with a very low output inpedance, and for these reasons normally encountered a-c fields do not pose a special problem. However, devices which radiate a wide band of frequencies such as an apparatus which produces a sputtering or spark type discharge can cause interference. Under most circumstances satisfactory operation may be insured by suitable shielding of the signal leads as indicated in Fig. 23. Note that twisted pair, two-conductor

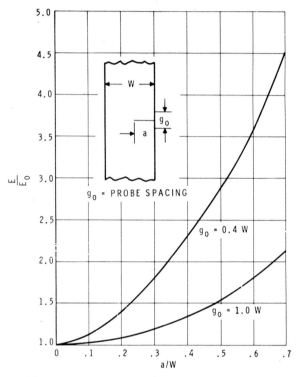

FIG. 24—*Calibration curves for converting electrical potential measurements to crack lengths for single-edge-crack-specimens.*

shielded cable is used and that the signal lead shield is connected only at the specimen. No general recommendations can be made concerning the instrument grounds. Substantial currents are frequently encountered circulating in steel building frames and water pipes, and for this reason it may be necessary to use a separate earth-ground isolated from the neutral side of the a-c line.

The electronically regulated constant-current supply may be replaced by a combination of a storage cell and a current controlling ballast resistor in series with the specimen. This resistor should have a low temperature coefficient and a resistance high relative to that of the specimen. While batteries provide a low-cost source of current, they lack the convenience of a good power supply. For example, changes in contact resistance will not influence the set output of the regulated power supply, but if sufficient in magnitude they will influence the current drawn from the batteries.

Previous recommendations made by the present authors included a description of yokes that clamped to the specimen and positioned the potential probes at a small fixed distance from the crack tip. These yokes

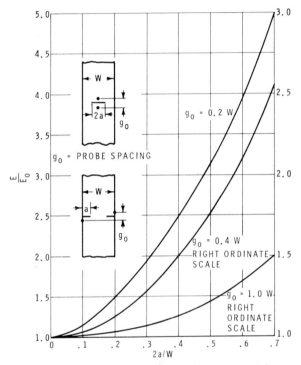

FIG. 25—*Calibration curves for converting electric potential measurements to crack lengths for symmetrically cracked plate specimens.*

were, of necessity, rather heavy, and consequently inertia forces tended to damage the probe points when a specimen ruptured, so that frequent resharpening of the points was necessary. The present practice is to fasten stainless steel wire at specified positions either side of the notch on the edges of edge-cracked tension and bend specimens. In the case of center-cracked specimens the wires are fastened to the specimen on either side of the crack at the centerline. These positions are further from the crack tip than those obtained using the previously described yokes. These new positions result in some loss in sensitivity; however, experience has shown that the sensitivity is more than adequate and that the measured potentials are less sensitive to small shifts in position of the pickup points. In the case of steel specimens the wires may be spotwelded to the specimen (stainless steel wire is convenient for this purpose) and the signal leads to the voltmeter-amplifier simply clipped onto the ends of these wires. For nonferrous metals the wires may be fastened by means of small screws fitting in tapped holes.

Calibration curves relating the ratio (E/E_0) of measured potential to the potential at zero crack length[9] to the relative crack length are shown in Figs. 24 and 25 for the new probe positions. It is important to note that the probe positions shown, the calibration curves for symmetrically cracked plate specimens (Fig. 25) will yield the average of the crack extension at each crack tip.

Acoustic Emission

Present techniques for detection of crack sounds [42] provide no way to relate the acoustic emission to the amount of crack propagation that has occurred. Also it may be difficult to eliminate sources of extraneous noise. At present the acoustic method best serves as a supplement to the previously described techniques. For example, the presence or absence of sound indicates whether a deviation in linearity of the load-displacement record is due to crack propagation on a fine scale or to plastic flow at the crack tip.

Comparison of the Methods

Advantages and limitations of various crack extension detection techniques were discussed previously [10]. However, a brief comparison of the three methods recommended for plane strain toughness testing should be helpful at this point. The acoustic method has the greatest inherent sensitivity to crack extension and responds only to actual crack movement. However, both the electric potential and displacement gage techniques have more than sufficient sensitivity for plane strain toughness testing. An electric potential measurement is not appreciably influenced by crack tip plastic flow except insofar as this changes the shape of the crack. Therefore nonlinearities in the load-potential record are almost entirely due to crack movement. The crack opening displacement, on the other hand, will be influenced by both crack tip plastic flow and crack extension. Nonlinearity in a load-crack opening displacement record therefore can be a reflection of either of these influences.

With the above thoughts in mind, it would seem desirable to use the displacement gage method in combination with a measurement of electric potential or acoustic emission. If only one technique is employed the most generally satisfactory will be that of measuring the crack opening

---

[9] A procedure for deriving E_0 from the measured initial crack length and the calibration curve is described in Ref 10.

displacement since it requires the least amount of complicated electronic gear and is most easily adapted to a variety of testing situations, particularly when tests are to be conducted at other than room temperature.

Criteria for Analysis of Load-Displacement Records

As discussed in the first section of this report, the K_{Ic} value is computed on the basis of the load corresponding to a well-defined unstable advance of the crack. The progress of crack extension with load during a test is generally followed by means of a linear displacement gage such as the one described in the preceding section. The analysis of load-displacement records requires the development of suitable popin criteria and methods of data analysis. However, before discussing these it is

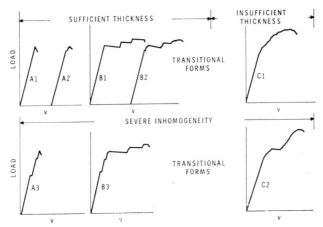

FIG. 26—*Typical load-displacement records illustrating several types of popin behavior.*

helpful to consider some of the complications associated with the problem and to outline the types of load-displacement records encountered in the NASA-NRL cooperative program.

It might be expected that a test specimen which met the size requirements outlined in the section on "Specimen Size Requirements" would exhibit a load-displacement record which was easily interpretable in terms of the load corresponding to the onset of unstable fracture under plane strain conditions. However, such ideal behavior is not always realized.

In what follows it will be assumed that the commonly described popin behavior illustrated schematically in Fig. 2 is obtained. This type of behavior was observed for the alloys tested thus far in the NASA-NRL cooperative program and therefore characterizes the data shown in the section on "Specimen Size Requirements." However, it is important to realize that this behavior will not be encountered for all engineering alloys. For example, SAE 4340 steel tempered at temperatures above about 750 F does not exhibit distinct popin steps but rather a gradually developing crack extension to maximum load, the amount of which decreases with increasing thickness. Only a relatively small amount of information is available concerning alloys exhibiting such characteristics, and it is not yet clear whether the methods of analysis to be discussed in this section will apply to them.

Types of Load-Displacement Records

Typical load-displacement records are shown in Fig. 26 for a series of tests on specimens of various thickness. If the specimen is sufficiently thick and the material homogeneous, the load-displacement diagram will be essentially linear to maximum load as shown by record *A1*. In this case the K_{Ic} value is equal to the K_I value computed on the basis of the maximum load and the initial crack length. The fracture surface of a specimen yielding this type of record will exhibit little or no shear lips. Material inhomogeneities encountered in most wrought alloys can produce small increments of crack extension at loads close to the maximum as indicated by record *A2*. In many instances, the magnitude of this "pre-cracking" will be very small, and K_{Ic} computed on the basis of the maximum load will then represent a useful measure of the fracture toughness for the bulk of the material in the specimen. On the other hand, if the alloy structure is strongly laminated or contains large particles of a randomly dispersed second phase, isolated bursts of crack extension of appreciable magnitude may occur at loads substantially less than the maximum as shown by record *A3*. In this record one or more distinct popins are observed well below the maximum load separated by portions of the curve showing no crack extension. Behavior of this type may indicate considerable variability in the fracture properties of the sample. Thus, an identical specimen taken from another location might rupture completely at a load near that corresponding to the first popin of record *A3*. Obviously, the significance of these small steps in the *A3* type record depends on the size and distribution of the structural units which fracture to produce the indications.

If the thickness of the specimen is barely sufficient to produce an *A1* type record, then reducing this thickness by perhaps one half may result in records of Type *B* shown in Fig. 26. These records are also readily interpretable in that they consist of a well-defined large popin followed by several bursts of crack extension that lead to complete rupture with only a moderate increase in the load. The effects of inhomogeneities are again revealed by steps in the load-displacement diagram preceding final rupture as indicated by records *B2* and *B3*. These steps have the same significance as when observed in Type *A* records.

With further reduction in specimen thickness, the load-displacement

records change from the easily interpretable Type *B* to presently unin-
terpretable types such as *C*. This change in popin behavior corresponds
to a thickness-dependent fracture mode transition. Thus, if the thickness
of a specimen giving a Type *B* record is reduced by, say, a factor of about
four, distinct popin indications may become completely indefinite, as in
the *C1* type record in Fig. 26. This record is characterized by an initial
smooth deviation from linearity followed by a steeply rising curve made
up of segments containing steps which are of the same magnitude as
or smaller than the precracking which characterized record Types *A2* and
B2. These small, indefinite steps, coupled with the steep continuous rise
in load to final rupture, indicate that crack extension is accompanied
by considerable plastic flow. It is not possible to derive a value of K_{Ic}
from such a record because sufficient plastic flow accompanies initial

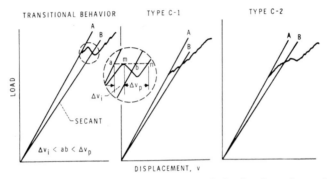

FIG. 27—*Examples of load displacement records for bend specimens illustrating suggested criteria for analysis of popin records.*

crack movement to relax the constraints responsible for plane strain
conditions at the crack tip. Occasionally a record of Type *C2* is encountered, which is similar to *C1* except for the relatively large step which is
preceded by considerable cracking under rising load. This behavior is
frequently observed when gross inhomogeneities are present such as the
various zones in a welded structure. Under these circumstances the ad-
vancing crack front may suddenly break through a brittle region and
then be arrested. Such records cannot be analyzed to yield useful K_{Ic}
data because of the excess plastic flow accompanying the fracture process
preceding the apparent popin.

Between the readily analyzable records of Types *A* and *B* and the
unanalyzable Type *C* lie transitional forms. These exhibit some nonlinearity preceding a popin indication of rather small magnitude which
is followed by a large amount of crack extension under rising load. Some
of these records can yield useful K_{Ic} data, while others should be re-
jected. It is in this transition region that popin criteria are needed.

Criteria and Data Analysis

Popin criteria and data analysis procedures should be compatible with the principles of linear elastic fracture mechanics and yet be adaptable to an uncomplicated and objective procedure for analysis of test records. The limitations of our present knowledge require a cautious approach to this problem. Specifically, it is important to have a method that will insure the discarding of records such as *C1* and *C2* which may yield K_{Ic} values that are too high. In formulating a procedure, attention was given to the large number of trial K_{Ic} tests made during the course of the NASA-NRL cooperative program. A related study of plane strain crack toughness test methods was published recently by Hanna and Steigerwald [*42a*]. Unfortunately, most of the tests made by these investigators did not satisfy the criteria for K_{Ic} testing that are proposed in this report. Furthermore, no quantitative criterion for estimating the adequacy of a popin indication is given in Ref *42a*. Otherwise, the conclusions reached are in general agreement with those of the present report.

The suggested data analysis procedure may be illustrated with the load-displacement records[10] shown in Fig. 27, which are typical of those obtained with bend specimens. The basis for the development of this procedure is given in Appendix I. The first step is to construct the secant *OB*. The reciprocal slope of *OB* should be larger than that of the initial linear portion *OA* by 6 per cent in the case of single-edge-crack tension or bend specimens provided a_0/W is about 0.5, and 2 per cent in the case of center- or double-edge-cracked tension specimens, provided $2a_0/W$ is about 0.5. For other values of a_0/W the slope of *OB* can be obtained by reference to the development given in Appendix I.

This secant establishes the upper limit on permissible deviation from linearity, Δv_i, preceding the popin indication. A popin indication is defined as a temporary maximum in the load-displacement curve followed by increase of the displacement without the load rising above this maximum value. To meet the requirement on deviation from linearity, this load maximum must lie between the lines *OA* and *OB* ($\Delta v_i < ab$). The actual appearance of the popin indication will depend on the combined stiffness of the specimen and tensile machine. In Fig. 27 the record illustrating transitional behavior corresponds to a relatively compliant bend specimen, and the load drops abruptly at popin. If the stiffness of the tensile machine were decreased sufficiently, the load would remain essentially constant during popin as indicated by the horizontal line *mn*. For the present purposes the popin displacement Δv_p is taken equal to the horizontal distance *mn* between the point of maximum load and the

---

[10] A similar procedure can be developed for load-potential records. However, as discussed in the section on "Instrumentation," the potential measurement is quite insensitive to crack tip plastic flow and for this reason is not recommended for general K_{Ic} testing.

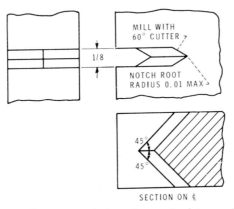

FIG. 28—*Chevron notch for edge-crack plate specimens.*

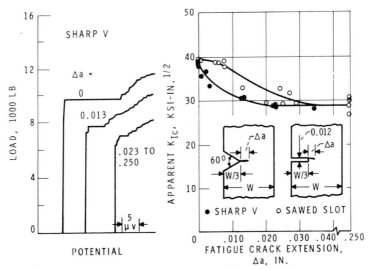

FIG. 29—*Influence of amount of fatigue crack extension from starter notches on apparent K_{Ic} and popin behavior for 7075-T651 aluminum alloy.*

load displacement curve. If Δv_p is at least equal to the maximum permissible deviation from linearity (distance *ab*), the popin is considered to be satisfactory.

Of the records shown in Fig. 27, that representing transitional behavior is acceptable because a popin step of sufficient size could be found that was not preceded by excessive deviation from linearity. The K_{Ic} calculated from such a record is considered valid provided the specimen dimensions meet the requirements outlined in the section on "Specimen Size Requirements" and provided proper precautions were followed regarding specimen preparation and testing procedure. Neither records of Type *C1* or *C2* are acceptable. In the case of *C1* no step of the required size can be found, and in the case of *C2* excessive deviation from linearity precedes popin. In Appendix I examples are given of the analysis of actual load-displacement records.

Specimen Preparation and Testing

This section is concerned with those aspects of specimen preparation and testing which require special attention in order to insure satisfactory accuracy in plane strain fracture toughness measurements with the practical specimen types detailed in Appendix II. A considerable amount of general information of specimen preparation and testing was given previously [10], and what follows is an attempt to up-date this material.

Fatigue Crack Starter Notches

The details of starter notches given previously [10] have been found generally satisfactory. However, the authors now prefer, where possible, to use a chevron notch starter of the type shown in Fig. 28 for edge-cracked specimens. This geometry has the advantage of a very high stress concentration at the chevron tip which insures that the fatigue crack can be started in a reasonable length of time at a low stress. The radius at the base of the chevron is 0.01 in. max, a value easily achieved with conventional milling or grinding equipment.

The fatigue crack should be extended sufficiently beyond the starter notch that the crack tip stress field is not influenced by the notch shape. No information exists to closely establish the required distance. However, experiments made with both sharp V-notches and square-ended narrow slots as starters show that large extensions are not necessary. According to Fig. 29, the apparent K_{Ic} value for 7075-T6 aluminum alloy is between 38 and 40 ksi·(in.)$^{1/2}$ for single-edge-notch specimens containing V-notches with a 0.00025-in.-root radius or slots made with a 0.012-in.-thick jeweler's saw. With progressive fatigue crack extension from the starter, the apparent K_{Ic} value decreases to a constant value between 28 and 31 ksi·(in.)$^{1/2}$. The amount of fatigue crack extension required to produce a constant K_{Ic} value should be larger the milder the discontinuity represented by the starter, and this effect is observed in Fig. 29, with the sawed slot requiring the greater extension.[11] It is interesting to note that the magnitude of the popin as revealed by the load-potential records shown in Fig. 29 is very large for the sharp machined notch and decreases with increasing fatigue crack extension from this notch. For either the V-notch or the sawed slot, a fatigue crack extension of somewhat more than 30 mils appeared to remove the crack front

---

[11] A larger scatter is observed for the data from the saw-slotted specimens because the effective radius of a sawed slot varies depending on the degree of roughness produced at the slot tip, which will be a function of the sharpness of the saw and the pressure applied by the operator.

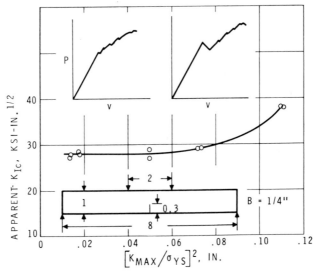

FIG. 30—*Effect of estimated $(K_{max}/YS)^2$ during fatigue cracking on the apparent K_{Ic} and popin behavior for 7075-T651.*

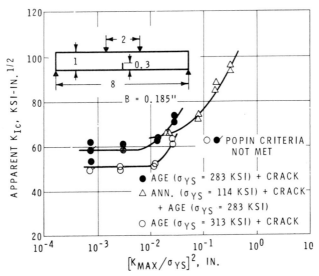

FIG. 31—*Effect of estimated $(K_{max}/YS)^2$ during fatigue cracking on apparent K_{Ic} of maraging steel cracked before or after aging.*

from the influence of the starter configuration. For chevron notches having the specified root radius, a fatigue crack extension of 0.050 in. (beyond the intersection of the chevron with the surface) would be more than adequate. When using tension-tension loading to develop fatigue cracks, application of an initial precompression of about one half the maximum tensile fatigue stress will be helpful in reducing the number of load cycles necessary to start the crack. Tests in the authors' laboratory indicate this procedure will not influence the K_{Ic} value for specimens fatigue cracked in the proper manner. Some investigators have used water or other corrosive media to assist in starting the crack. This procedure should be useful provided it can be shown that the corrosive medium does not influence the final results. In some materials an electric discharge machined slot has proven to be a very effective starter in comparison with a machined slot of the same width.

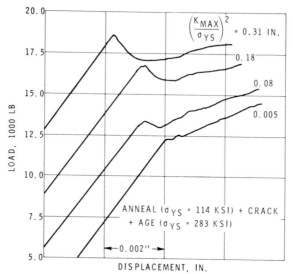

FIG. 32—*Effect of estimated $(K_{max}/YS)^2$ on the popin behavior of maraging steel bend specimens cracked before aging.*

Fatigue Cracking

The effective "sharpness" of a fatigue crack depends on the maximum stress intensity, K_{max}, imposed during fatigue cracking. The effect of increasing K_{max} beyond a certain level is to increase the apparent K_{Ic} of the material. The magnitude of this effect depends on the alloy, and the fatigue cracking conditions should be such that the crack sharpness is not less than is likely to be encountered in service. In this respect, it is considered that $(K_{\mathrm{max}}/\sigma_{\mathrm{YS}})^2$ is an important parameter influencing the "sharpness" of the fatigue crack.

From general considerations it would be desirable to use a high stress intensity range, ΔK, for fatigue cracking in order to achieve the highest crack propagation rate commensurate with adequate control of the process. On the other hand, the ratio of $(K_{\mathrm{max}}/\sigma_{\mathrm{YS}})^2$, where K_{max} is the maximum fatigue stress intensity, should be sufficiently low that further reduction in the ratio would not affect the measured K_{Ic} value.

Some indication of the effect of $(K_{max}/\sigma_{YS})^2$ on the apparent K_{Ic} and on the popin behavior is shown by recent tests made by the authors in which the fatigue cracking load applied to bend specimens was varied. The bend specimens were provided with a chevron notch and were fatigue cracked in cantilever bending (at 3600 rpm) with the notch located directly over the support. Tension-tension loading was employed, the ratio of minimum to maximum load being one third for all specimens. Tests were made on 283 ksi yield strength maraging steel, fatigue cracked before or after aging, and on 7075-T651 aluminum alloy. In representing these data, the apparent K_{Ic} values have been plotted against $(K_{max}/\sigma_{YS})^2$,

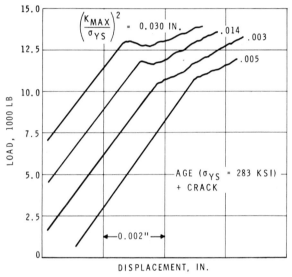

FIG. 33—*Effect of estimated* $(K_{max}/YS)^2$ *on the popin behavior of maraging steel bend specimens cracked after aging.*

where K_{max} is the estimated stress intensity factor in fatigue calculated from the maximum applied tension load using the K calibration for three-point bending (see the section on "K Calibrations of Specimens"). This way of calculating K in cantilever bending does not account properly for the boundary conditions but provides the best available estimate.

According to Fig. 30 the apparent K_{Ic} value for 7075-T651 is essentially independent of $(K_{max}/\sigma_{YS})^2$ for values of this ratio up to about 0.05, and then rises with increasing K_{max}. The magnitudes of the popin indications were considerably larger at the higher K_{max} levels, as indicated by the insets in the figure. In contrast, the apparent K_{Ic} of the maraging steel specimens when aged before cracking, Fig. 31, was independent of $(K_{max}/\sigma_{YS})^2$ only up to a value of this ratio of about 0.01. It should be noted that attempts to fatigue crack such specimens at $(K_{max}/\sigma_{YS})^2 =$

0.050 resulted in popin during fatigue cracking, and K_{Ic} results for these specimens are not reported. The data for the same maraging steel when cracked before aging are also shown in Fig. 31 but is not sufficient to establish an upper limit on $(K_{max}/\sigma_{YS})^2$ below which the apparent K_{Ic} would be independent of this ratio. However, the data do indicate the apparent K_{Ic} for specimens cracked before aging begins to level out at $(K_{max}/\sigma_{YS})^2$ of about 0.02. The influence of the fatigue cracking conditions on the popin behavior is illustrated by the load-displacement

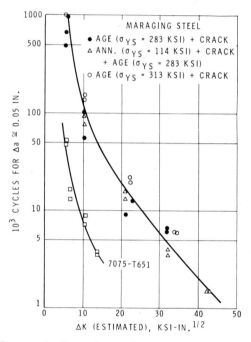

FIG. 34—*Influence of* ΔK *on the number of tension-tension fatigue cycles to produce a total crack extension of 0.050 in. in bend specimens.*

curves shown in Figs. 32 and 33 for specimens cracked before and after aging, respectively. As was observed for the 7075-T651 aluminum alloy, there is a pronounced increase in the amount of crack extension at popin with increase of $(K_{max}/\sigma_{YS})^2$ for the maraging steel specimens when cracked in either condition.

The fatigue crack extension Δa in the above-described test specimens terminated about 0.050 in. beyond the intersection of the chevron notch with the specimen surface. The total number of cycles necessary to produce these cracks is shown in Fig. 34 as a function of the estimated ΔK (equal to $\tfrac{2}{3} K_{max}$). For the maraging steel cracked either before or after aging the total number of cycles is the same function of ΔK within the limits of scatter. At a given ΔK the aluminum alloy requires considerably fewer cycles than the steel to produce a crack of the same length. Comparing Fig. 34 with Fig. 31 it is seen that at least 30,000 cycles (8 min at 3600 rpm) are required to produce an adequately sharp crack in the maraging steel aged before cracking. In contrast, adequately sharp cracks in the aluminum alloy can be produced in about 10,000 cycles (3 min).

In summary, the results of these illustrative experiments show that the fatigue cracking conditions can have a pronounced effect on K_{Ic}. High values of $(K_{\mathrm{max}}/\sigma_{\mathrm{YS}})^2$ during fatigue can produce exaggerated popin indications and an elevated apparent plane strain crack toughness. These effects may be thought of in terms of crack blunting, in that the same type of behavior is observed for specimens provided with sharp machined notches (compare Figs. 32 and 33 with Fig. 29). Additional data are clearly needed to better define the influences of the conditions of fatigue crack generation on the plane strain fracture behavior. Until more definitive information is available, it would seem desirable to fatigue crack specimens at the lowest value of $(K_{\mathrm{max}}/\sigma_{\mathrm{YS}})^2$ commensurate with producing the cracks in an acceptable time. The required number of cycles may be minimized by fatigue cracking the specimens in the condition in which they are to be tested, without any intervening stage of heat treatment. The fatigue load range should not be greater than required to produce an average rate of crack extension of about 0.05 in. in 50,000 cycles, and the mean load should be as low as possible, in no case greater than two thirds of the load range. These criteria should provide reasonable assurance that the fatigue crack is adequately sharp. When an intervening stage of heat treatment between fatigue cracking and testing is unavoidable, the effect of fatigue cracking conditions on the K_{Ic} test results should be checked directly.

Face Grooving

Several years ago Newhouse and Wundt [43] described a Charpy impact specimen provided with a brittle surface layer produced by nitriding. The purpose of this brittle layer was to suppress the formation of plastic zones at the side boundaries and thereby more closely approach plane strain fracture conditions at the crack front. Wei and Lauta [44] have made use of carbonitriding in fracture toughness tests. More recently, Freed and Krafft [45] have suggested that face grooving of plate specimens for K_{Ic} testing would accomplish the same purpose and be applicable to any material. Empirical correction procedures have been proposed by these authors for the application of planar K calibrations to specimens with face grooves.

The effects of face grooving have not been adequately studied, but the complexity is apparent. If the grooves are sufficiently deep, crack initiation will occur at the corners between the crack front and the face grooves where the stress intensity is highest. As the ratio of groove depth to

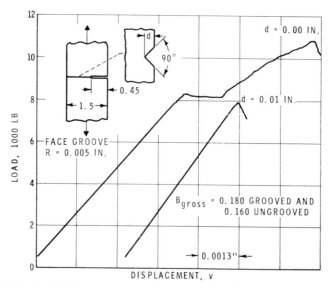

FIG. 35—*Load-displacement records from single-edge-crack tension specimens with and without face grooves (280 ksi yield strength maraging steel).*

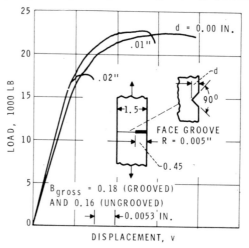

FIG. 36—*Load-displacement records from single-edge-crack tension specimens with and without face grooves (195 ksi yield strength maraging steel).*

specimen thickness is decreased, the variation of K across the crack front is decreased, and the crack front will tend to advance uniformly. What is desired is some optimum groove depth and sharpness that will adequately suppress side boundary plastic zone formation and yet produce a nearly uniform advance of the crack front. It is difficult to see how this optimum depth can be determined, and it will probably be different for different materials.

If the specimen is sufficiently anisotropic in its fracture characteristics, the fracture can originate at the face grooves and propagate across the thickness of specimen. This possibility, of course, increases with the depth and sharpness of the face grooves.

The effect of face grooving on the load-deflection record is illustrated in Figs. 35 and 36 for maraging steel (not listed in Table 1) at two yield strength levels, tested using 1.5-in.-wide, single-edge-crack specimens. Shallow face grooves (the ratio of gross to net thickness, $B/B_N = 1.1$ or 1.3) with a 0.005-in.-root radius were employed. The gross thickness was 0.180 and 0.160 in. for grooved and ungrooved specimens, respectively. When aged at 850 F for 8 hr ($\sigma_{YS} = 280$ ksi), Fig. 35, a distinct popin is observed without face grooves, and the grooved specimen ($B/B_N = 1.1$) ruptures completely at a load slightly lower than the ungrooved specimen. The K_{Ic} values for these two specimens are in reasonable agreement according to the method of calculation suggested in Ref 45. When aged at 700 F for 8 hr ($\sigma_{YS} = 195$ ksi), Fig. 36, the ungrooved specimen exhibits no distinct popin, and the record would be discarded by applying the criteria presented in the section "Criteria for Analysis of Load-Displacement Records." With increasing depth of face groove, the maximum load is progressively lowered and the record chopped off. However, if the criteria of the section "Criteria for Analysis of Load-Displacement Records" are applied, all of the records in Fig. 36 exhibit excessive deviation from linearity and should be discarded.

On the basis of the results so far available it is not clear whether face grooving can usefully increase the K_{Ic} measurement capacity of a plate specimen. However, it can produce abrupt rupture under conditions where a distinct popin followed by considerable stable crack extension would characterize an ungrooved specimen of the same net thickness. Instrumentation would still be required in order to judge the validity of a K_{Ic} value derived from a face-grooved specimen. However, it is not known whether the same criteria for analysis of load-displacements records can be applied to face-grooved specimens as have been suggested for ungrooved specimens.

Considering all the complications discussed above, it appears that in order to achieve useful results, the depths, and possibly also the root radii, of the face grooves should be tailored to the material and specimen geometry. In this respect, the use of face grooves is a matter for further research rather than a technique to be generally applied in plane strain fracture toughness testing.

Pin Friction Effects in Bending

Pin friction will tend to increase the measured K_{Ic} value over what would be obtained in the absence of friction. Since there is no satisfactory way of correcting for friction effects in a given test setup, the best procedure is to minimize the effect of pin friction by proper design of the loading fixture.

The following is a brief description of some results obtained in the authors' laboratory from a series of tests made to determine methods of minimizing friction effects in bending. Strain-gaged bend specimens without notches were employed in these tests. The relative influence of changes in the loading arrangements on the friction effect was judged by comparing the measured stress (obtained from the measured strain and the elastic modulus) with the value calculated from the applied load using the elementary flexure formula. The effect of friction will, of course, be revealed by a calculated stress higher than the measured stress. It should be noted that this method cannot be used to accurately assess the error in K which would be associated with a particular loading arrangement because the manner of deformation and therefore the

TABLE 4—*Results of tests to determine friction effects on 4-point bending*

Span-to-Width Ratio	Setup[a]	Per Cent Error
8:1	free pins	0.5
4:1	free pins	0.5
8:1	V-blocks[c]	3.5
8:1	fixture[b]	1.0
4:1	fixture	0.5

[a] Minor span: $\frac{9}{16}$-in.-diameter pins on 2-in. centers.
Major span: $\frac{3}{4}$-in.-diameter pins on 3-in. or 4-in. centers.
[b] See Fig. 37 for details of fixture.
[c] Major span pins in V-blocks fixed to a base plate and minor span pins fixed in a loading yoke.

contribution of friction to the measured load will be different in a cracked specimen than in a smooth specimen.

Tests of the type just described were made on 7075-T651 aluminum bend specimens[12] approximately 10 in. long, 1 in. wide, and $\frac{1}{4}$ in. thick. The tension and compression surfaces were finish ground, and a $\frac{1}{8}$-in.-long foil strain gage was bonded to the tension surface at the center of the span. The specimens were loaded in four-point bending with a major span of either 8 or 4 in. and a minor span of 2 in. An X-Y plotter provided a load-strain record on loading (to 1500 lb) and unloading for each test setup investigated. The loading portion of these records was quite linear in all cases, and the calculated stresses were compared with the measured stresses on the basis of the maximum applied load. Generally the effect of friction was to produce hysteresis in the load-strain diagram; however, under some conditions the loading

[12] The tension modulus of 7075-T6 ($E = 10.3 \times 10^6$ psi) given in Ref 46 agrees with that reported by the authors in a previous paper [13].

and unloading records were linear and coincident even though the calculated stress was greater than the measured stress.

The most pertinent results obtained are summarized in Table 4, which gives the errors in the calculated stresses as compared with the measured values for five different test setups. If all pins are free to roll on flat hardened steel plates, the error in the calculated stress is within the ±0.5 per cent repeatability of replicate measurements of the strain. A condition of high friction is represented by the tests in which the minor span pins are fixed in a loading yoke and the major span pins fixed in V-blocks clamped to a base plate. The error encountered with this setup was 3.5 per cent.

Bend test fixtures can be constructed to permit sufficient movement of the pins so that frictional effects are negligible. In a plane strain fracture toughness test the required movements of the pins will be small,

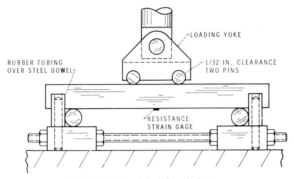

FIG. 37—*Modified bend fixture.*

and it is possible to accommodate these and yet prevent the major span pins from being forcibly expelled on complete fracture of the specimen. An example of modification of an existing bend fixture to permit small pin movements is illustrated in Fig. 37. This figure shows a fixture that positions the major span pins against vertical dowels (two on each side) and supports the minor span pins in a loading yoke. The major span is adjustable by means of threaded tie bars. Conditions closely approaching those characteristic of free pins were obtained by (1) covering the vertical dowels with $\frac{1}{16}$-in. wall thickness surgical tubing and (2) making the holes in the loading yoke $\frac{1}{32}$ in. greater in diameter than the minor span pins. For these conditions the maximum error in the calculated stress (Table 4) was 1 per cent.

The bend test fixture modification described above illustrates the generally useful principle that frictional effects in four-point bending can be minimized by permitting small outward movements of the major span pins and corresponding inward movements of the minor span pins.

There are, of course, several ways of incorporating these requirements in the initial fixture design. A design suggested by M. Jones of NASA-Lewis is shown in Fig. 38. The major and minor span pins are retained in slots by small springs. These slots have a width somewhat greater than the pin diameter in order to permit the necessary pin movements. The springs position the pins against accurately located corners of the slots which establish the major and minor spans. The major span support blocks are adjustable by means of pins fitting into locating holes in the base plate.

Friction effects in three-point bending are difficult to investigate by the types of tests described above. These difficulties arise from the

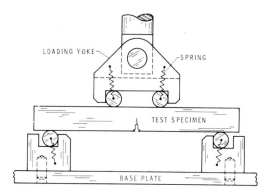

FIG. 38—*Suggested design of bend fixture permitting pin movement.*

fact that the flexure formula applied to three-point bending leads to inaccuracies in the calculated stresses. The errors involved increase with a decrease in the span-to-width ratio of the three-point loaded beam and, as shown by Frocht [47], may amount to as much as 12 per cent for a span-to-width ratio of 4:1. While approximate solutions to the stresses in three-point loaded beams have been developed [48], it is unlikely that tests of the type described above using three-point loading are necessary. Thus, for given specimen dimensions and equal bend angles, three-point loading should result in no larger friction effects than observed for four-point loading, and a fixture suitable for four-point loading should work equally well in three-point loading.

APPENDIX I

Basis for the Analysis of Load-Displacement Records

The purpose here is to develop a rational method for analyzing load-displacement records for (1) excessive deviation from linearity preceding popin and (2) sufficiency of the popin indication. A typical load-displacement record is shown in Fig. 39 which also shows the various quantities involved in the analysis. Popin is indicated by the load maximum P_p followed by an increasing displacement Δv_p with decreasing load. The displacement v_i is that which would have corresponded to P_p if the record had remained linear up to this point. The additional displacement Δv_i is the combined result of several effects and cannot be analyzed precisely; instead this deviation from linearity will be regarded as though it were entirely due to an increment of crack extension Δa_i .

In order to establish a permissible limit for $\Delta a_i/a_0$ it is assumed that Δa_i

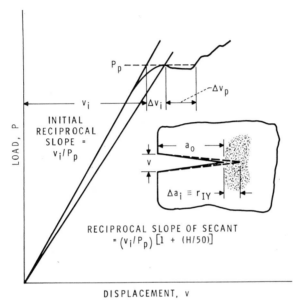

DISPLACEMENT, v

FIG. 39—*Typical load displacement record showing quantities involved in development of a procedure for load-displacement record analysis.*

should not exceed the formally computed plane strain plastic zone correction term. That is

$$\Delta a_i \leqq r_{\mathrm{Iy}} \cong 0.05 \left(\frac{K_{\mathrm{Ic}}}{\sigma_{\mathrm{YS}}}\right)^2$$

Also, for a valid test it was assumed that

$$a_0 \geqq 2.5 \left(\frac{K_{\mathrm{Ic}}}{\sigma_{\mathrm{YS}}}\right)^2$$

Hence, for a satisfactory test

$$\frac{\Delta a_i}{a_0} \leqq \frac{1}{50} \quad \dots\dots\dots\dots\dots\dots\dots (3)$$

This condition may be expressed in terms of the displacement by use of experimentally determined calibration curves which relate the displacement per unit load to the crack length for each particular specimen type. The calibration relation takes the form

$$\frac{vEB}{P} = F\left(\frac{a}{W}\right)$$

where $F(a/W)$ is a function of a/W for single-edge-cracked specimens which depends on the specimen characteristics.[13] Consequently, at constant load

$$\frac{\Delta vEB/P}{vEB/P} = \frac{\Delta v}{v} = \frac{F\left(\frac{a}{W} + \frac{\Delta a}{W}\right) - F\left(\frac{a}{W}\right)}{F\left(\frac{a}{W}\right)}$$

or considering that $\Delta a \ll a_0$

$$\frac{\Delta v_i}{v_i} = \frac{1}{F} \frac{dF}{d\left(\frac{a_0}{W}\right)} \frac{\Delta a_0}{W}$$

and therefore

$$\frac{\Delta v_i}{v_i} = \left[\frac{a_0}{W} \frac{1}{F} \frac{dF}{d\left(\frac{a_0}{W}\right)}\right] \frac{\Delta a_i}{a_0} \quad\dots\dots\dots\dots\dots (4)$$

Combining Eq 3 with Eq 4 gives the allowable limit of deviation from linearity in terms of displacements

$$\frac{\Delta v_i}{v_i} \leq \frac{1}{50} \frac{a_0}{W} \frac{1}{F} \frac{dF}{d\left(\frac{a_0}{W}\right)} = \frac{H}{50}$$

where H is a calibration factor derived from the experimentally determined calibration curves given in Figs. 20 to 22. Plots of this factor are given in Fig. 40 for several specimen types. It should be noted that the relation between H and a/W will be independent of the gage length provided this is less than the crack length.

The limitation on deviation from linearity may be expressed in terms of the reciprocal slope of a secant line connecting the maximum load point P_p at popin to the origin. Thus

$$\frac{\Delta v_i + v_i}{P_p} \leq \frac{v_i}{P_p}\left[1 + \frac{H}{50}\right] \quad\dots\dots\dots\dots\dots (5)$$

For the recommended range of values of a_0/W between 0.45 and 0.55, the value of $H/50$ might be standardized at 0.06 for single-edge-crack tension and bend specimens and at 0.02 for the center- and double-edge-crack specimens. This leads to the requirement that a deviation from linearity should represent a reciprocal slope change on a plot of load versus displacement, of not more than 6 per cent for the single-edge-crack specimens and not more than 2 per cent for the symmetrically cracked specimens.

---

[13] In the case of the center- and double-edge-cracked specimens, vEB/P is expressed as a function of $2a/W$.

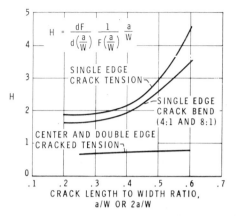

FIG. 40—*Calibration factors for use in analysis of load displacement records.*

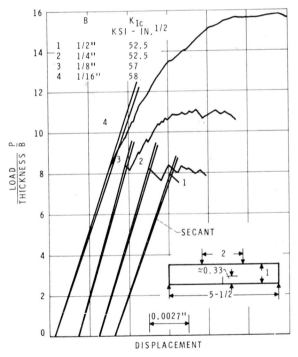

FIG. 41—*Examples of analyses of load-displacement records for several thicknesses of SAE 4340 bend specimens.*

The question of how large a popin indication should be required can only be answered in an empirical way at this time. Ideally, the advance of the crack front at popin should include an amount of material at least sufficient to be representative of the bulk fracture properties of the specimen (that is, substantially greater than the size and spacing of minor phase particles in an alloy and extending beyond the small zone of altered material produced during fatigue cracking). This distance will, of course, be different for different materials and probably will also vary with the fatigue cracking and testing conditions. A good deal of additional experience is necessary before firm guidelines can be established for the required extent of popin. Analysis of the trial K_{Ic} tests made during the NASA-NRL cooperative program indicate that a displacement change at popin, Δv_p, at least equal to the maximum permissible deviation from linearity at the popin load is a reasonably conservative criterion for a satisfactory popin indication. Application of this criterion will probably ensure that the bulk fracture properties of the specimen are being measured for most engineering alloys tested using specimens meeting the size requirements outlined in the section "Specimen Size Requirements."

Examples of the analyses of actual load-displacement records are illustrated in Fig. 41, which shows results obtained from bend tests on specimens of four thicknesses of SAE 4340H steel (600 F temper, σ_{YS} = 230 ksi) machined from a single 1-in. plate. In order to permit convenient representation of all records on one figure, an ordinate scale of load divided by thickness P/B has been used.

Referring to Fig. 40, a value of H = 1.75 is obtained for the nominal a_0/W of 0.33 used for these specimens. As discussed above, this leads to a requirement that the deviation from linearity preceding popin shall correspond to an increase in the reciprocal slope of the secant of not more than 3.5 per cent. The secant lines in Fig. 41 are drawn in conformance with this requirement, and the selected popin loads are indicated for each record. Of the records illustrated, those for specimens of ⅛ in. or thicker meet the requirements on deviation from linearity and magnitude of popin indication. The record for the ¹⁄₁₆-in.-thick specimen meets neither of these requirements, and the popin load was selected at the first definite step.

The average K_{Ic} value for duplicate tests at each thickness is also shown on Fig. 41. It will be noted that the ¼ and ½ in.-thick specimens give an average K_{Ic} = 52.5 ksi·(in.)$^{1/2}$, while the thinner specimens give higher values. This trend of K_{Ic} with thickness is in accordance with the observations made in the section on "Specimen Size Requirements" which would indicate a thickness of at least 0.14 in. would be necessary for a valid K_{Ic} test on this alloy.

APPENDIX II

Specimen Types

The suggested proportions of the various plane strain crack toughness test specimens discussed in the text are shown in Figs. 42 through 45. Only one bend specimen is illustrated, Fig. 43, which has a span-to-width ratio (S/W) of 4 and is subjected to three-point loading. It is considered inadvisable to use bend specimens with substantially lower values of S/W since the K calibrations for such specimens would likely have dubious accuracy and because the errors introduced by friction increase with decreasing S/W. However, there is no reason why higher values of S/W can not be used. Except for the increased load requirements, there is no disadvantage to four-point bending. The preferred range of thickness for plate specimens between $W/2$ and $W/4$ does not represent a basic requirement for a valid K_{Ic} test but is suggested for convenience in arriving at a graded series of specimen sizes.

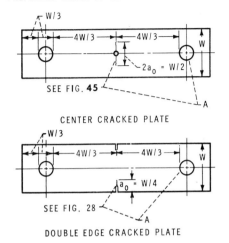

FIG. 42—*Proportions for center- and double-edge-cracked plate specimens. A-surfaces must be symmetric to specimen centerline within W/1000.*

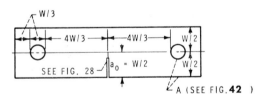

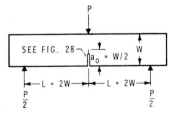

FIG. 43—*Proportions for single-edge-cracked tension and bend specimens.*

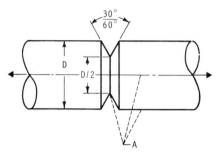

CIRCUMFERENTIALLY CRACKED ROUND BAR
RADIUS OF MACHINED NOTCH = 0.005 IN. MAX

FIG. 44—*Proportions for the circumferentially cracked round bar. A-surfaces must be concentric with the load axis to within D/1000.*

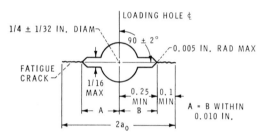

FIG. 45—*Fatigue crack starter for center-cracked plate specimens.*

APPENDIX III

Notation

a, a_0 Length, half length, or half diameter of crack according to type of specimen; subscript 0 refers to actual value

Δa, Δa_i Increment of crack extension; subscript i refers to initial increment

A Net cross-sectional area of cracked Charpy specimen

B Thickness of plate or bend specimen

d Diameter of crack-notched section of circumferentially cracked round bar

D Shank diameter of circumferentially cracked round bar

E Young's modulus; *also* the difference in electric potential difference between probe positions

g, g_0 Distance between two gage points used for relative displacement measurement; subscript 0 refers to initial gage length for unloaded specimen

$\mathcal{G}_{Ic}$ Critical strain energy release rate with crack extension per unit length of crack front, mode I or opening mode

H Half height of crackline loaded specimen; also, dimensionless calibration factor (see Appendix I)

K, K_I Stress intensity factor; subscript I denotes opening mode of crack extension

ΔK Stress intensity range in fatigue cracking
K_{Ic} Plane strain crack toughness
K_{max} Maximum stress intensity in fatigue cracking
M Bending moment
P Load
P_p Load at popin
r_y, r_{Iy} Plastic zone correction term; subscript I refers to plane strain; without subscript refers to plane stress
S Support span of bend specimen; *also* standard deviation
v, v_i Relative displacement of two gage points; subscript i refers to linearly extrapolated value at popin (see Fig. 39)
Δv_i, Δv_p Increments of relative displacement (see Appendix I)
W Width of plate specimen or depth of bend specimen
$\overline{X}$ Mean value
Y Dimensionless stress intensity coefficient
ν Poisson's ratio
σ Applied stress
σ_{YS} Yield strength
ϕ Crack shape parameter for semielliptical surface cracks

References

[1] "Fracture Testing of High-Strength Sheet Materials," *ASTM Bulletin*, No. 243, January, 1960, p. 29, also No. 244, February, 1960, p. 18.
[2] "The Slow Growth and Rapid Propagation of Cracks," *Materials Research & Standards*, Vol 1, 1961, p. 389.
[3] "Fracture Testing of High-Strength Sheet Materials," *Materials Research & Standards*, Vol 1, 1961, p. 877.
[4] "Screening Tests for High-Strength Alloys Using Sharply Notched Cylindrical Specimens," *Materials Research & Standards*, Vol 2, 1962, p. 196.
[5] "Progress in Measuring Fracture Toughness and Using Fracture Mechanics," *Materials Research & Standards*, Vol 4, 1964, p. 107.
[6] *Fracture Toughness Testing and Its Applications, ASTM STP No. 381*, Am. Soc. Testing Mats., 1965.
[7] G. R. Irwin, "Plastic Zone Near a Crack and Fracture Toughness," Proceedings of the Seventh Sagamore Ordnance Materials Research Conference, *Report No. MeTE 661-611/F*, Syracuse University Research Inst., August, 1960, p. IV-63.
[8] R. W. Boyle,, A. M. Sullivan, and J. M. Krafft, "Determination of Plane Strain Fracture Toughness with Sharply Notched Sheets," *Welding Journal Research Supplement*, Vol 41, 1962, p. 428s.
[9] F. A. McClintock and G. R. Irwin, "Plasticity Aspects of Fracture Mechanics," *Fracture Toughness Testing and Its Applications, ASTM STP 381*, Am. Soc. Testing Mats., 1965, p. 84.
[10] J. E. Srawley and W. F. Brown, Jr., "Fracture Toughness Test Methods," *Fracture Toughness Testing and Its Applications, ASTM STP 381*, Am. Soc. Testing Mats., 1965, p. 133.
[11] G. R. Irwin and J. A. Kies, "Critical Energy Rate Analysis of Fracture Strength," *Welding Journal Research Supplement*, Vol 33, 1954, p. 193s.
[12] J. D. Lubahn, "Experimental Determination of Energy Release Rate for Notch Bending and Notch Tension," *Proceedings*, Am. Soc. Testing Mats., Vol 59, 1959, p. 885.
[13] J. E. Srawley, M. H. Jones, and B. Gross, "Experimental Determination of the Dependence of Crack Extension Force on Crack Length for a Single-Edge-Notch Tension Specimen," *Technical Note D-2396*, NASA, August, 1964.

[14] B. Gross, J. E. Srawley, and W. F. Brown, Jr., "Stress-Intensity Factors for a Single-Edge-Notch Tension Specimen by Boundary Collocation of a Stress Function," *Technical Note D-2395*, NASA, August, 1964.

[15] B. Gross and J. E. Srawley, "Stress-Intensity Factors for Single-Edge-Notch Specimens in Bending or Combined Bending and Tension by Boundary Collocation of a Stress Function," *Technical Note D-2603*, NASA, January, 1965.

[16] B. Gross and J. E. Srawley, "Stress-Intensity Factors for Three-Point Bend Specimens by Boundary Collocation," *Technical Note D-3092*, NASA December, 1965.

[17] P. C. Paris and G. C. Sih, "Stress Analysis of Cracks," *Fracture Toughness Testing and Its Applications, ASTM STP 381*, Am. Soc. Testing Mats., 1965, p. 30.

[18] R. G. Forman and A. S. Kobayashi, "On the Axial Rigidity of a Perforated Strip and the Strain Energy Release Rate in a Centrally Notched Strip Subjected to Uniaxial Tension," *Journal of Basic Engineering*, Vol 86, 1964, p. 693.

[18a] O. L. Bowie, "Rectangular Tensile Sheet with Symmetric Edge Cracks," *Paper 64-APM-3*, Am. Soc. Mechanical Engrs., 1964.

[19] B. Gross and J. E. Srawley, "Stress-Intensity Factors by Boundary Collocation for Single-Edge-Notch Specimens Subject to Splitting Forces," *Technical Note D-3295*, NASA, February, 1966.

[20] M. J. Manjoine, "Biaxial Brittle Fracture Tests," *Paper 64-Met-3*, Am. Soc. Mechanical Engrs., May, 1964.

[21] R. E. Johnson, Panel discussion, *Fracture Toughness Testing and Its Applications, ASTM STP 381*, Am. Soc. Testing Mats., 1965, p. 399.

[22] W. K. Wilson, "Analytical Determination of Stress Intensity Factors for the Manjoine Brittle Fracture Test Specimen," *Report No. WERL-0029-3*, Westinghouse Research Laboratories, August, 1965.

[23] W. K. Wilson, "Optimization of WOL Brittle Fracture Test Specimen," *Report No. 66-1B4-BTLFR-R1*, Westinghouse Research Laboratories, January, 1966.

[24] E. J. Ripling, panel discussion, *Fracture Toughness Testing and Its Applications, ASTM STP 381*, Am. Soc. Testing Mats., 1965, p. 396.

[25] S. Mostovoy, P. B. Crosley, and E. J. Ripling, *Use of Crack Line Loaded Specimens for Measuring Plane Strain Fracture Toughness*, Materials Research Laboratory, Inc., January, 1966.

[26] H. F. Bueckner, "Coefficients for Computation of the Stress Intensity Factor K_I for a Notched Round Bar," *Fracture Toughness Testing and Its Applications, ASTM STP 381*, Am. Soc. Testing Mats., 1965, p. 82.

[27] H. W. Liu, "Discussion on Critical Appraisal of Fracture Mechanics," *Fracture Toughness Testing and Its Applications, ASTM STP 381*, Am. Soc. Testing Mats., 1965, p. 23.

[28] W. F. Brown, Jr., "Comments on K_c Data Used in the 5th Fracture Committee Report," notes to ASTM Special Committee on the Fracture Testing of High Strength Metallic Materials, April 24, 1964.

[29] E. L. Crow, F. A. Davis, and M. W. Maxfield, "Statistics Manual," *Report No. 3369*, Naval Ordnance Test Station, 1960.

[30] D. E. Driscoll, "Reproducibility of Charpy Impact Test," *Impact Testing, ASTM STP 176*, Am. Soc. Testing Mats., 1955, p. 70.

[31] A. M. Sullivan, "New Specimen Design for Plane-Strain Fracture Toughness Tests," *Materials Research & Standards*, Vol 4, 1964, p. 20.

[32] J. E. Srawley and C. D. Beachem, "The Effect of Small Surface Cracks on Strength," Proceedings of the Seventh Sagamore Ordnance Materials Research Conference, *Report No. MeTE 661-611/F*, Syracuse University Research Inst., 1960, p. IV-169.

[33] J. E. Srawley and C. D. Beachem, "Fracture of High Strength Sheet Steel Specimens Containing Small Cracks," *Evaluation of Metallic Materials in*

Design for Low Temperature Service, ASTM STP 302, Am. Soc. Testing Mats., 1961, p. 69.

[33a] C. F. Tiffany and P. M. Lorenz, "An Investigation of Low-Cycle Fatigue Failures Using Applied Fracture Mechanics," *Report No. ML-TDR-64-53*, Boeing Co., May, 1964.

[33b] C. F. Tiffany, P. M. Lorenz, and L. R. Hall, "Investigation of Plane-Strain Flaw Growth in Thick-Walled Tanks," *NASA CR-54837*, Boeing Co., February, 1966.

[33c] G. R. Irwin, "Crack Extension Force for a Part-Through Crack in a Plate," *Journal of Applied Mechanics*, Vol 84E, No. 4, December, 1962.

[34] P. N. Randall, "Severity of Natural Flaws as Fracture Origins," *Report No. STL-4439-6006-RU-000 (DDC No. AD-472891)*, TRW Space Technology Laboratories, October, 1965.

[35] A. S. Kobayashi, M. Ziv, and L. R. Hall, "Approximate Stress Intensity Factor for an Embedded Elliptical Crack Near Two Parallel Free Surfaces," *International Journal of Fracture Mechanics*, Vol 1, 1965, p. 81.

[35a] F. W. Smith, "Stresses Near a Semicircular Edge Crack," Ph.D. thesis, University of Washington, December, 1965.

[36] A. S. Kobayashi, "On the Magnification Factors of Deep Surface Flaws," *Structural Development Research Memo No. 16*, Boeing Co., December, 1965.

[37] C. E. Hartbower and G. M. Orner, "Metallurgical Variables Affecting Fracture Toughness in High-Strength Sheet Alloys," *AFASD TDR-62-868*, Man Labs Inc., June, 1963.

[38] D. Kalish and S. A. Kulin, "Thermomechanical Treatments Applied to Ultra-High Strength Steels," *Final Technical Report*, Man Labs, Inc., Bureau of Naval Weapons Contract NOW-64-0356-C, April, 1965 (available from DDC as *AD-614806*).

[39] J. M. Krafft, unpublished note to the ASTM Committee on Fracture Testing of High Strength Metallic Materials, Aug. 29, 1963.

[40] J. M. Krafft, "A Rate Spectrum of Strain Hardenability and Fracture Toughness," *Report of NRL Progress*, 1966, p. 6 (available from Clearinghouse for Scientific and Technical Information).

[41] D. M. Fisher, R. T. Bubsey, and J. E. Srawley, "Design and Use of Displacement Gage for Crack Extension Measurements," *Technical Note D-3724*, NASA, November, 1966.

[42] M. H. Jones and W. F. Brown, Jr., "Acoustic Detection of Crack Initiation in Sharply Notched Specimens," *Materials Research & Standards*, Vol 4, 1964, p. 120.

[42a] G. L. Hanna and E. A. Steigerwald, "Development of Standardized Test Methods to Determine Plane Strain Fracture Toughness," *AFML TR-65-213*, TRW Inc., September, 1965.

[43] D. L. Newhouse and B. M. Wundt, "A New Fracture Test for Alloy Steels," *Metal Progress*, Vol 78, 1960, p. 81.

[44] R. P. Wei and F. J. Lauta, "Measuring Plane-Strain Fracture Toughness with Carbonitrided Single-Edge-Notch Specimens," *Materials Research & Standards*, Vol 5, 1965, p. 305.

[45] C. N. Freed and J. M. Krafft, "Effect of Side Grooving on Measurements of Plane Strain Fracture Toughness," report to ASTM Committee E-24, May 12, 1965.

[46] *Alcoa Aluminum Handbook*, Aluminum Company of America, Pittsburgh, Pa., 1962.

[47] M. M. Frocht, "A Photoelastic Investigation of Shear and Bending Stresses in Centrally Loaded Simple Beams," *Bulletin of the Carnegie Institute of Technology*, 1937.

[48] S. Timoshenko and J. N. Goodier, *Theory of Elasticity*, 2nd edition, McGraw Hill Book Co., New York, 1951, p. 99.

DISCUSSION

The authors wish to thank the discussers for their kind remarks and for adding a considerable amount of valuable information to the subject of plane strain crack toughness testing. Because of the rather large volume of discussion and because of the number of subjects treated, the authors replies follow each discussion of a given subject.

M. J. Manjoine[1]—This discussion is an amplification of the characteristics of the "crackline loaded single-edge-cracked specimens." The method of loading does not adequately describe the Manjoine specimen which is used by the Westinghouse Electric Corp.[2] even though it is currently called WOL (Wedge Open Loading) specimen.[3] A review of the original design and its stress analysis will illustrate the high degree of "constraint" which is achieved in this "compact" specimen.

The constraint is greater for this specimen than that of other single-edge-cracked specimens such as the SEN because of the biaxial loading, illustrated in Fig. 46. The original geometry was selected so that the ratio of the nominal loading stresses, $\sigma N_2/\sigma N_1$, is about 0.85. Although the loading is biaxial, the stresses are triaxial (Fig. 47) as determined by photoelastic measurements.[4] These curves give the principle stresses (as a ratio of the nominal stress σN_1) plotted as a function of x/d, where x is the distance from the crack tip (along the crackline) divided by the ligament length, d. The middle curve illustrates the high constraint developed in the Manjoine specimen in the region just below the notch where the three principle stresses are nearly equal. For a distance from 1 to 3 per cent of the net section, the maximum deviation of any of the principle stresses from the mean stress is less than 16 per cent. Thus, the action of this region is one of restricting the plastic zone size. This has been evident in test programs with specimens of various sizes in which valid K_{Ic} have been measured even though the ratio of K_{Ic}/σ_{YS} was greater than 1.0.

Although the original size and geometry have been found to be adequate for several materials with K_{Ic}/σ_{YS} approaching one, the load de-

[1] Westinghouse Electric Corp., Astronuclear Labs., Pittsburgh, Pa.

[2] M. J. Manjoine, "Biaxial Brittle Fracture Tests," *Journal of Basic Engineering Transactions*, ASME, June, 1965, pp. 293–298.

[3] W. K. Wilson, "Optimization of WOL Brittle Fracture Test Specimen," *Research Report 66-1B4-BTLFR-R1*, Westinghouse Research Laboratories, January, 1966.

[4] M. M. Leven, "Stress Distribution in the M4 Biaxial Fracture Specimen," *Research Report 65-1D7-STRSS-R1*, Westinghouse Research Laboratories, March, 1965, Fig. 18. Plastic model 4 times Manjoine specimen in size.

flection curve for materials of higher K_{Ic}/σ_{YS} becomes nonlinear before fracture and problems arise in analyses of the curves, as described in the paper. An experimental study of the Manjoine specimen showed that this nonlinearity was mainly caused by plastic bending in the specimen arms; therefore, a modification was made to reduce this bending. An optimization study was also undertaken[5] to achieve the minimum specimen volume for a $\sigma N_2/\sigma N_1 = 0.8$. This quantity was selected as a reasonable value from other studies and resulted in a modified specimen

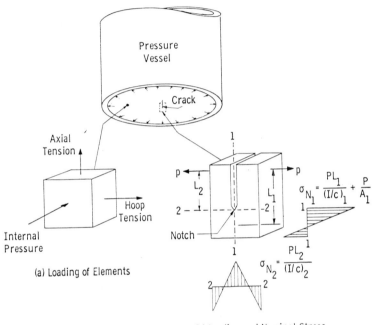

(a) Loading of Elements

(b) Loading and Nominal Stress
Distribution of Test Specimen

FIG. 46—*Simulation of pressure vessel crack loading by biaxial test specimen.*

with a H/W of 0.48 and $a/W = 0.35$. The K calibrations of the original and modified designs based on collocation calculations are given in Fig. 48, together with the curves for H/W of 0.4 and 0.5, as given in Fig. 8. There are many considerations in an optimization study; however, we can profit by reviewing the large volume of work already completed by the Westinghouse Corp.[3-5] The authors of the paper suggest that a/W and H/W be selected at about 0.6; from the points in Fig. 48, it can be seen that the optimization study[3] yielded a smaller a/W when H/W

[5] W. K. Wilson, "Analytical Determination of Stress Intensity Factors for the Manjoine Brittle Fracture Test Specimen," *Report No. WERL-0029-3,* Westinghouse Research Laboratories, August, 1965.

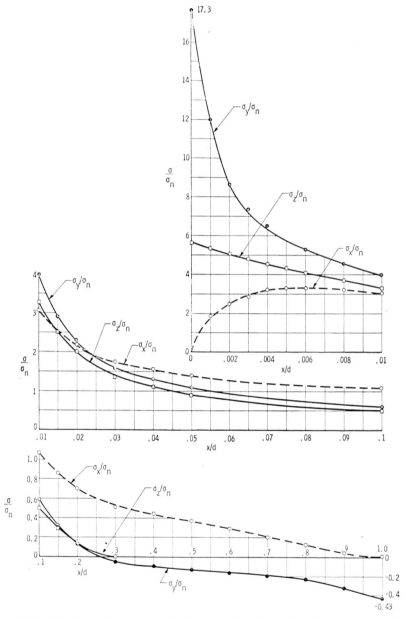

FIG. 47—*Distribution of principal stresses along the section of symmetry ox for the center section of model obtained from slice B3.*

was increased. Therefore, if the advantages of the constraint of this specimen are to be maintained, large deviations from the investigated designs should not be made.

Another important consideration is the change in the factor Y caused by a change in a/W. At a low a/W, the curves of Fig. 48 (also those of Fig. 8) have a low slope and, therefore, much smaller changes in the factor Y than for those at $a/W = 0.6$. Thus, more accurate values of K_I can be determined for a low a/W for the nominally small deviations due to plastic zone size and dimension measurement errors.

Finally, I wish to repeat that in the five years of study and testing with

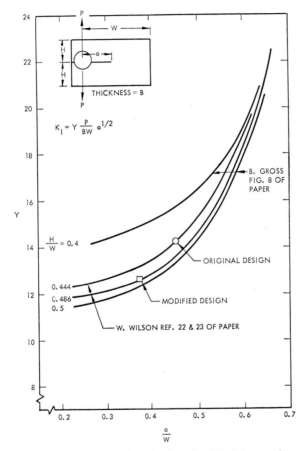

FIG. 48—*Collocation K calibrations for Manjoine specimen.*

the Manjoine specimen, a considerable amount of reliable data has been obtained[6-14] particularly for materials of higher K_{Ic}/σ_{YS}. Since all of us

[6] J. A. Jan, "Fatigue Cracking of WOL Fracture Toughness Specimens," *Research Report 65-1P6-FRATM-M1*, Westinghouse Research Laboratories, August, 1965.

[7] R. E. Johnson, "Fracture Mechanics: A Basis for Brittle Fracture Prevention," *Report WAPD-TM-505*, Westinghouse Bettis Atomic Power Laboratory, November, 1965.

[8] W. K. Wilson, "Comparison of Stress Distribution on the Plane of Symmetry

wish to advance the development of fracture toughness measurement, we should build on this past experience and data.

E. J. Ripling[15]—The authors are to be complimented for writing a particularly clear paper. They appear to have successfully systematized our knowledge in a particularly confusing area. Presumably because their paper is limited to the current status of plane crack toughness testing, they found it convenient to treat the less well established crackline loaded specimens as a single item. This may lead to some confusion, however, since the two types of such specimens discussed in the paper (the Manjoine (WOL) design and the Ripling-Mostovoy (DCB) design), although similar in appearance, are almost opposite in performance. The curve of K calibration for the WOL specimen rises rapidly as a is increased with constant W, Fig. 8, because the specimen compliance results almost exclusively from the hinging action of the unbroken ligament; as the crack gets longer the specimen gets softer at an increasing rate. The compliance value of the DCB specimen (Figs. 24 and 25), on the other hand, is determined by the bending of the arms that lie above and below the crack plane. Consequently, the K calibration curves for the two types of specimens are completely different. Since the compliance is dictated by the beam shape, it is possible to contour the DCB specimen such that the toughness is a function of load only, that is, independent of a. For such specimens, the K calibration is not conveniently plotted in terms of the dimensionless parameters Y and a/W as the authors have done, but rather as Y' and a, Fig. 49, where Y' has the dimensions in.$^{-3/2}$. It is obvious that the use of this specimen eliminates the need for either crack length or compliance measurements during the test.

---

of the WOL Test Specimen Obtained by Various Methods and an Interpretation of the Results of a Photoelastic Study," *Research Report 66-107-MEMTL-R2*, Westinghouse Research Laboratories, January, 1966.

[9] A. M. Wahl, M. M. Leven, and W. K. Wilson, "Energy Release Rate for Biaxial Brittle Fracture Test Specimen," *Research Report WERL-8844-1*, Westinghouse Research Laboratories, May, 1963.

[10] A. J. Bush and W. K. Wilson, "Determination of Energy Release Rate for Biaxial Brittle Fracture Specimen," *Research Report WERL-8844-2*, Westinghouse Research Laboratories, August, 1964.

[11] G. O. Sankey and J. H. Bitzer, "Plane Strain Fracture Toughness Measurements of Three A302B Materials by Means of Spin Test," *Research Report WERL-8844-3*, Westinghouse Research Laboratories, December, 1964.

[12] A. J. Bush and R. B. Stouffer, "Fracture Toughness Tests on A302B Steel," *Research Report WERL-8844-9*, Westinghouse Research Laboratories, October, 1965.

[13] E. T. Wessel and W. H. Pryle, "Investigation of the Applicability of the Biaxial Brittle Fracture Test for Determining Fracture Toughness," *Research Report WERL-8844-11*, Westinghouse Research Laboratories, August, 1965.

[14] W. G. Clark, Jr., "Ultrasonic Detection of Fracture Initiation and Extension in the WOL Type Fracture Toughness Specimen," *Research Report 66-1B4-BTLFR-P2*, to be presented to Society of Non-Destructive Testing, Chicago, Ill., Nov. 1, 1966.

[15] Materials Research Laboratory, Richton Park, Ill.

W. F. Brown, Jr., and J. E. Srawley (authors)—The respective contributions of Messrs Manjoine and Ripling to the development and application of crackline loaded single-edge-crack specimens are well known, and their discussions raise some interesting points. While Mr. Ripling wishes to emphasize the difference between the DCB and WOL designs, we prefer to regard them as particular examples of a single, broad class of specimens, as illustrated by Fig. 50. The plotted points in this figure are

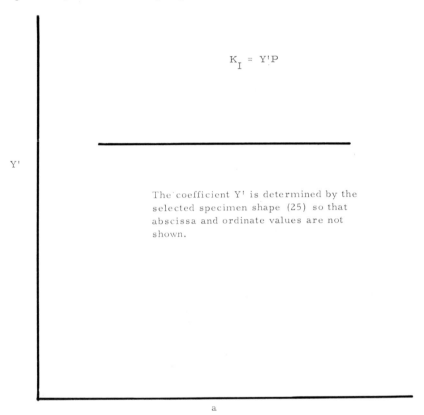

$$K_I = Y'P$$

Y'

The coefficient Y' is determined by the selected specimen shape (25) so that abscissa and ordinate values are not shown.

a

FIG. 49—*Calibration curves plotted for two types of specimens.*

boundary collocation computations [*19*] of the stress intensity coefficient $KBW^{1/2}/P$ versus a/W for two crackline loaded specimens of the same uniform height $2H$, and different widths $2H$ and $5H$. The slender specimen is like that used by Mr. Ripling, and the squat specimen close to that originated by Mr. Manjoine. The curved line represents what Mr. Ripling calls "the hinging action of the unbroken ligament," and is, in fact, a simple adaptation of the solution for a semifinite crack approaching the free edge of a half plane given by Paris and Sih (Eq 181 of Ref *17* of our paper). We find that this solution fits the boundary collocation results fairly well for all crackline loaded specimens when the crack approaches the far boundary. The two straight lines both correspond to the relation $KB/P = 3.45 (a + 0.7H)/H^{3/2}$, which is expressed in terms of $KBW^{1/2}/P$ versus a/W in Fig. 50 in order that it can be shown in conjunction with the "hinge action" curve.

The boundary collocation results for the squat specimen lie on the

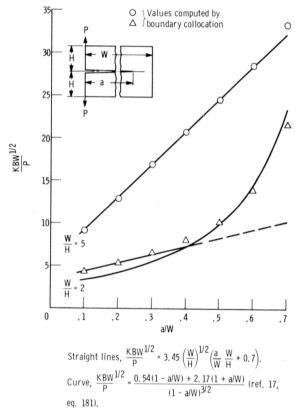

Straight lines, $\dfrac{KBW^{1/2}}{P} = 3.45 \left(\dfrac{W}{H}\right)^{1/2}\left(\dfrac{a}{W}\dfrac{W}{H} + 0.7\right)$.

Curve, $\dfrac{KBW^{1/2}}{P} = \dfrac{0.54(1 - a/W) + 2.17(1 + a/W)}{(1 - a/W)^{3/2}}$ (ref. 17, eq. 181).

FIG. 50—*Stress intensity coefficients for two selected examples of crackline loaded single-edge-crack specimens.*

straight line for values of a/W up to 0.3, then tend to follow the curve. The results for the slender specimen lie on the straight line for values of a/W up to 0.6, then diverge toward the part of the curve which is not shown in the figure. The respective behaviors of the two specimens, therefore, are different only in degree, not in kind. Since a/W in the WOL specimen is usually about 0.4, it is not true that the dominant effect in this specimen is the "hinge action."

The linear relation represented by the two straight lines in Fig. 50 is an empirical fit to boundary collocation results (see Ref *19* of our paper), and it is important to appreciate that it cannot be deduced satisfactorily from calculations of the bending of the specimen arms. While the compliance of the specimen may depend predominantly on the bending of the arms, the rate of change of compliance with crack length depends predominantly on the deformation of that part of the specimen near the crack tip. In other words, in treating a crackline loaded specimen as a joined pair of cantilevers it has to be realized that the end effect is the predominant effect, not merely a minor correction. A close analogy is a long, narrow centercracked specimen, in which only the central region near the crack has any appreciable effect on the rate of change of compliance with crack length.

Figure 50 also shows that the K calibration curves can be conveniently plotted in terms of dimensionless parameters, in this case $KBW^{1/2}/P$ versus a/W, and the same is true for any beam contour. Alternatively, $KBH^{1/2}/P$ could be plotted against a/H. Both forms show clearly the degree to which K is dependent on a for any desired specimen shape.

The choice of specimen slenderness ratio, W/H, depends on the purpose of the specimen. For K_c testing we would normally prefer a low slenderness ratio because any unnecessary width is simply wasted material. It is admittedly sometimes possible to use a specimen for more than one K_{Ic} test if the first test is interrupted just after popin; however, we would then consider it necessary to generate a new fatigue crack before proceeding with a second test. Another objection to slender specimens is that they require deep face grooves to prevent the crack from turning away from its initial direction. We have discussed our objections to face grooves in the paper and elsewhere in the discussion.

The WOL specimen is fairly well proportioned for K_{Ic} testing, but we cannot agree with Mr. Manjoine that there is no margin for improvement. The optimization study which he mentions involved a concept of specimen efficiency used in our earlier review (Ref 10), but which we have since abandoned in favor of our present approach. The main point in this connection is that we no longer employ so-called nominal stresses, which are superfluous in the context of linear elastic fracture mechanics and tend to confuse the issues. Our suggestion of a/W and H/W each equal to 0.6 was stated to be tentative, and we plan to test several variations. One of our objectives is to dispense with the somewhat elaborate stud and pin loading arrangement of the WOL specimen and to use two-pin loading instead. This would necessitate some modification of Mr. Manjoine's original proportions.

We would agree with Mr. Manjoine that one factor to be considered in the choice of specimen proportions is the sensitivity of K to crack length. On the other hand, we cannot go as far as Mr. Ripling when he suggests that a specimen so contoured that K was independent of a would eliminate the need for instrumentation. The instrumentation serves the essential purpose of revealing the course of crack extension during the critical stage of the test. If all materials behaved in an ideal manner by fracturing abruptly in K_{Ic} tests then we could dispense with instrumentation. Unfortunately, it appears that most materials do not behave in this way and that standardization of K_{Ic} testing will probably have to involve a definite but arbitrary procedure analogous to that specified for the determination of the 0.2 per cent offset yield strength. We can no more dispense with instrumentation in K_{Ic} testing than we can in tension testing, and we believe that it is a disservice to fracture toughness testing to encourage the idea that a "blind" test can serve any useful purpose. This is not to say that contoured specimens have no value for other purposes, such as fatigue crack propagation rate measurements.

With regard to Mr. Manjoine's point about the triaxiality of the stress field in the near vicinity of the crack front, we are inclined to believe that the degree of triaxiality may be somewhat greater in a crackline loaded specimen than in remotely loaded specimens. We do not think the question can be properly resolved until the three-dimensional stress fields of different types of specimens have been compared. The photoelastic studies of the WOL specimen conducted at Westinghouse Research Laboratories are admirable and ought to be extended to include other specimen types. The triaxiality issue is important because the basic fracture criterion is not known, and it could depend upon the degree of triaxiality as well as on the stress intensity. Recently we have obtained a few K_{Ic} results with crackline loaded specimens (both WOL and DCB types) which were consistently about 15 per cent lower than results obtained with bend specimens on identical materials. This difference might be connected with a higher degree of triaxiality in the crackline loaded specimens. This would not mean, however, that one group of results was more correct than the other, but rather that we should re-examine our concepts. Furthermore, it should not represent any impediment to K_{Ic} testing for materials evaluation and strength calculations if it is clearly recognized that the K_{Ic} crack toughness is a somewhat arbitrary property, just like the yield strength.

Mr. Manjoine suggests that five years of study and testing with the crackline loaded specimen at Westinghouse has provided a considerable amount of reliable K_{Ic} data, particularly for materials with a high ratio of K_{Ic}/σ_{YS}. Examination of his references does indeed indicate a substantial amount of valuable information has been generated, particularly concerning the three dimensional state of stress in this specimen. However, very little data were obtained which would permit comparison of K_{Ic} values from this type of specimen with those from other types. Data of this nature are essential in order to determine whether or not K_{Ic} is a constant independent of specimen geometry, and therefore whether or not "valid" plane strain crack toughness values are being measured.

W. K. Wilson[16]—This discussion is concerned with the regions of validity of the K_I described stress field for some of the specimen geometries recommended by the authors. As pointed out in Ref *27* by H. W. Lin and again emphasized by the authors, K_I will give an adequate single parameter representation of the fracture process if the crack tip plastic zone is sufficiently small in comparison with the region around the crack tip in which K_I adequately describes the elastic stress field. At present a study[17], is underway to determine these regions of validity

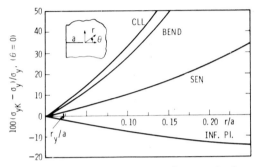

FIG. 51—*Deviation of σ_{yK} on the $\theta = 0$ plane.*

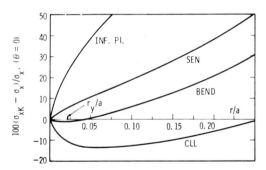

FIG. 52—*Deviation of σ_{xK} on the $\theta = 0$ plane.*

for various specimen geometries. Although only limited results are available at present, it is of interest to consider them here.

The available results are shown in Figs. 51 and 52. The indicated curves for different specimen types show the per cent deviation on the $\theta = 0$ plane (indicated in Fig. 51) of σ_{yK} and σ_{xK}, the K described stresses, from σ_y and σ_x, the actual elastic stresses. The per cent deviation, σ_{yK} and σ_{xK}, have the following forms

[16] Mechanics Dept., Westinghouse Electric Corp., Research and Development Center, Churchill, Pittsburgh, Pa.
[17] Westinghouse Research and Development Laboratories.

$$\% \ (\text{Dev})_y \ = \ 100 \ \frac{\sigma_{yK} - \sigma_y}{\sigma_y}, \ \text{etc.}$$

$$\sigma_{yK} = \sigma_{xK} = \frac{K}{2\pi r} \ \text{at} \ \theta = 0$$

The four types of specimens considered are the single-edge-cracked plate in tension (SEN), single-edge-cracked plate in bending (BEND), crackline loaded single-edge specimen (CLL), and an infinite plate subject to uniform uniaxial tension and containing a crack of finite length perpendicular to the stress field (INF PL). The dimensions for the SEN and BEND specimens are those recommended by the authors in Table 3 ($a = W - a = 2.5 \ (K_{Ic}/\sigma_{YS})^2$). The dimensions of the CLL specimen are $a = W - a = H = 2.5 \ (K_{Ic}/\sigma_{YS})^2$. The dimensions of the INF PL. are $a = 2.5 \ (K_{Ic}/\sigma_{YS})^2$ where the total crack length in this case is $2a$. The infinite plate containing the crack roughly represents a centercracked plate under uniform tension having the dimensions given in Table 3. The stresses for the SEN, BEND, and CLL specimens were determined by boundary collocation, and the stresses for the cracked infinite plate specimen were obtained by use of Inglis's solution.[18] For all four specimens the extent of the plastic zone in the $\theta = 0$ plane will be approximately $r_Y/a = 1/(15\pi)$. This point is indicated in Figs. 51 and 52.

Although no definite conclusions regarding required specimen size can be drawn from Figs. 51 and 52, a couple of general conclusions can be made. It appears that the region of validity of the K described stress field is rather limited, and therefore the use of large specimens as recommended by the authors is necessary. These curves also suggest that the use of the same crack lengths and specimen width for different types of specimen geometries is only a first order approximation. Therefore, the writer suggests that further experimental optimization of all types of specimens be carried out prior to establishing a tentative recommended practice.

Messrs. Brown and Srawley—Mr. Wilson's discussion relates to an important issue which we chose to avoid in our report in the interest of simplicity. The point is well made and requires no discussion other than to emphasize that our neglect of this particular issue is only one of several simplifying assumptions that are involved in the application of current fracture mechanics to real bodies. Until we have a better understanding of the three-dimensional distribution of stresses and strains in elastic-plastic-strain-hardening bodies we must be content with resolving some of the practical questions that arise by empirical methods. We are confident that advances in analysis over the next few years will substantially

[18] E. E. Inglis, "Stresses in a Plate Due to the Presence of Cracks and Sharp Corners," *Transactions*, Institution of Naval Architects, London, Vol 60, 1913, p. 219.

reduce the current heavy burden of testing for the purpose of establishing the limitations of the tests. We agree wholeheartedly with Mr. Wilson's general conclusions.

C. E. Feddersen[19]—From the perspective of design applications, the calibration factors (or finite-width corrections) are especially important elements of fracture mechanics theory. These expressions are the scaling transformations by which test data are extrapolated into practical design criteria. Since the precedents set by this committee have a far-reaching effect on the engineering applications, the following criticisms are offered in a constructive sense.

The comments may be resolved into two points about the calibration factors for the center-notch specimens. The first point concerns the leading coefficient of the calibration expression, Y. The coefficient 1.77 appears to be the value of $\sqrt{\pi}$. For clarity of interpretation and for

TABLE 5—*Finite width corrections.*
$$Y/\sqrt{\pi} = f(\lambda) \text{ where } \lambda = 2a/W$$

Author	Expression
Brown and Srawley	
3rd degree...........	$Y/\sqrt{\pi} = 1 + 0.128\lambda - 0.288\lambda^2 + 1.525\lambda^3$
2nd degree...........	$Y/\sqrt{\pi} = 1 - 0.1\lambda + \lambda^2$
Isida.....................	$Y/\sqrt{\pi} = 1 + 0.5948\lambda^2 + 0.4812\lambda^4 + \cdots + 0.2535\lambda^{14}$
Forman and Kobayashi...	$Y/\sqrt{\pi} = [\Sigma F(\lambda)g(\lambda)]^{1/2}$
Dixon...................	$Y/\sqrt{\pi} = (1 - \lambda^2)^{-1/2}$
Greenspan...............	$Y/\sqrt{\pi} = (1 - 0.5\lambda^2 - 0.5\lambda^4)^{-1}$
Modified Greenspan	
(Brossman and Kies)...	$Y/\sqrt{\pi} = (1 + 0.5\lambda^4)^{1/2}(1 - 0.5\lambda^2 - 0.5\lambda^4)^{-1}$
Irwin...................	$Y/\sqrt{\pi} = [(2/\pi\lambda) \tan (\pi\lambda/2)]^{1/2}$

consistency with fracture mechanics theory, it is considered better form to retain the leading coefficient as the symbol $\sqrt{\pi}$.

The second and more important point is concerned with the actual form of the calibration expressions. Consider Table 5, which lists a few of the popular expressions for the center-notch calibration in algebraic form. (Note that the term 1.77 has been transposed in the first expression for purposes of comparison). The Brown and Srawley expressions are considered compact expressions which closely match the Isida equation, now considered the most precise expression for center-notch specimens. The Forman and Kobayashi expression is another formulation which appears to substantiate that of Isida. The formulations of Dixon, Greenspan, and Brossman and Kies are others which have been utilized. The final expression, that of Irwin, is in present usage but is to be superseded by the first listed expressions of Brown and Srawley.

Now a question arises: "How different are these various formula-

---

[19] Battelle Memorial Inst., Columbus, Ohio.

tions?" To answer this, consider Table 6. Here, values of the calibrations are tabulated for discrete values of the aspect ratio, $\lambda = 2a/W$. Note that at the currently recommended aspect ratio of 0.33 for plane strain toughness testing the discrepancies are quite small. However, as the recommended aspect ratio for testing increases to 0.50, the discrepancies increase, and it is very desirable to approximate Isida's work as closely as possible.

TABLE 6—*Comparison of various finite width corrections.*

Aspect Ratio	Brown and Srawley		Isida	Forman and Kobayashi	Dixon	Greenspan	Modified Greenspan (Brossman and Kies)	Irwin
	3rd Degree	2nd Degree						
0 ..	1.000	1.00	1.000	. . .	1.000	1.000	1.000	1.000
0.1..	1.012	1.00	1.006	. . .	1.005	1.005	1.005	1.001
0.2..	1.026	1.02	1.025	. . .	1.021	1.029	1.029	1.017
0.3..	1.053	1.06	1.058	. . .	1.037	1.051	1.052	1.040
0.4..	1.103	1.12	1.109	. . .	1.091	1.101	1.107	1.076
0.5..	1.183	1.20	1.187	. . .	1.155	1.185	1.205	1.130
0.6..	1.303	1.30	1.303	. . .	1.250	1.324	1.370	1.208
0.7..	1.473	1.42	1.487	1.464	1.401	1.574	1.670	1.335
0.8..	1.699	1.56	1.799	. . .	1.667	2.135	2.370	1.565
0.9..	1.993	1.72	2.391	. . .	2.292	3.745	4.320	2.115
1.0..	2.365	1.90	3.631	. . .	∞	∞	∞	∞

TABLE 7—*Comparison of Isida and secant corrections.*

Aspect Ratio	Isida	$(\sec \pi\lambda/2)^{1/2}$	Difference
0	1.000	1.000	0
0.1	1.006	1.006	0
0.2	1.025	1.025	0
0.3	1.058	1.059	0.001
0.4	1.109	1.112	0.003
0.5	1.187	1.189	0.002
0.6	1.303	1.304	0.001
0.7	1.487	1.484	0.003
0.8	1.799	1.796	0.003
0.9	2.391	2.525	0.134
1.0	3.631	∞	∞

There exists a natural trigonometric function which approaches the Isida work more closely over a wider range than do the proposed Brown and Srawley results. This is shown in Table 7. Note that the precision appears to be within 0.3 per cent through an aspect ratio of 0.8. Here it is recommended that the secant expression be used to match Isida's work. In addition to greater accuracy over a wider range, the secant expression is certainly more compact than a second or third degree polynomial.

Now, a more subtle question appears: "From where does the secant correction arise?" With the simplification of notation $\theta = \pi\lambda/2$, we write the secant expression as

$$\left[\sec\theta\right]^{1/2} = \left[\frac{1}{\sin\theta}\cdot\tan\theta\right]^{1/2} \dots\dots\dots\dots\dots (6)$$

and compare it with the-current Irwin expression,

$$\left[\frac{1}{\theta}\cdot\tan\theta\right]^{1/2} \dots\dots\dots\dots\dots\dots (7)$$

There is a strong analytical similarity between these expressions through the usual trigonometric approximation $\theta \approx \sin\theta$, at small values of θ. While the Irwin analysis yielding Eq 7 is not questioned, it is suggested that there may exist a closely related stress function which would yield Eq 6.

However, whether it is an exact or approximate equation for matching Isida's work, the concise and accurate nature of the secant equation has considerable merit. The committee is also urged to survey the other calibration equations for simpler, more direct representations. Direct and concise format is certainly advantageous to the committee, as well as invaluable to those who will be applying the committee's developments.

Messrs. Brown and Srawley—For the practical purpose with which we are concerned in our paper we consider it desirable to express K calibrations in a simple standard form wherever possible. These calibrations are interpolation functions which are fitted to a limited number of primary results. The polynomial form permits determination of the coefficients of the interpolation function by a standard least-squares-best-fit computational procedure. It is also a convenient form for computation and manipulation.

We are indebted to Mr. Feddersen for his interesting observation that Isida's results for the center-cracked specimen correspond very closely to $(\sec \pi a/W)^{1/2}$; this is a convenient and compact expression. It seems most unlikely, however, that equally simple forms could be found for other configurations, and we are not aware of any methodical procedure that could be used to search for such forms.

From our point of view the expression of the polynomial coefficients in terms of the factor $\pi^{1/2}$ (1.77 ...) is an unnecessary embellishment. It amounts to the same thing as using the alternate stress intensity factor which is usually, but not always, written as a script K in the literature. The ASTM Special Committee on Fracture Testing (now E-24) decided early in its life to standardize on the K used in our paper in order to avoid ambiguity.

H. P. Chu[20]—The effect of fatigue cracking on fracture toughness depends on the extent of plastic deformation at the crack tip due to fatigue loading. In practice, the plastic deformation can be minimized by limit-

[20] U.S. Naval Marine Engineering Laboratory, Annapolis, Md.

ing the fatigue stress to a certain per cent of the yield strength of the material. An example can be given for a 2-in.[2] notched beam made of a quenched and tempered steel with 140,000 psi yield strength. By limiting the cyclic stress to about 50 per cent of the yield strength, an adequate fatigue crack could be produced after 2300 to 2700 cycles. The beams were subjected to three-point, tension-zero-tension loading.

The variability of K_{Ic} results can be much greater than that shown by the authors. A collection of K_{Ic} values of maraging steels[21] is shown here (Fig. 53) for comparison with the authors' data. The factors discussed in the authors' paper, such as specimen design and test methods, must have contributed a great deal to the scatter of data in Fig. 53, in addition

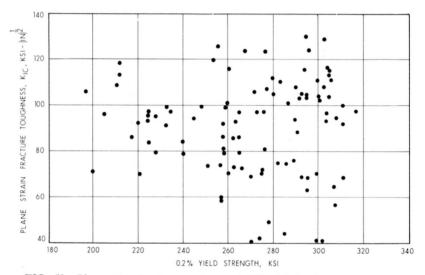

FIG. 53—*Plane strain fracture toughness of 18% nickel maraging steels at various yield strengths (from footnote 21).*

to the various alloy conditions tested. It shows that efforts to reduce scatter of K_{Ic} values are indeed in great demand.

Carman[22] has recently reported his test results of notched aluminum sheet specimens of different sizes. He concluded that "for the very high-strength aluminum alloys, the 4-in.-wide specimen is sufficiently large to give accurate values of fracture toughness." However, his data (Fig. 54) indicate that the G_c values of the 4-in.-wide specimens are consistently much lower than those of the 20-in.-wide specimens. How would

[21] M. F. Amateau and E. A. Steigerwald, "Fracture Characteristics of Structural Metals," *Final Report to Bureau of Naval Weapons ER-5937-3*, TRW Electromechanical Div., Cleveland, Ohio, Jan. 22, 1965, p. 59.
[22] C. M. Carman, "Crack Resistance Properties of High-Strength Aluminum Alloys," *Report R-1789*, Frankford Arsenal, Philadelphia, Pa., December, 1965, *DDC Document Ad-629-105*.

the authors account for such discrepancy in the light of their recommended specimen design and test requirements?

Messrs. Brown and Srawley—We are obliged to Mr. Chu for his dramatic illustration of the danger of uncritical acceptance of some of the alleged K_{Ic} values that have been reported in the literature. We are convinced of the importance of the fracture mechanics approach to materials evaluation, but we are concerned that the approach may be

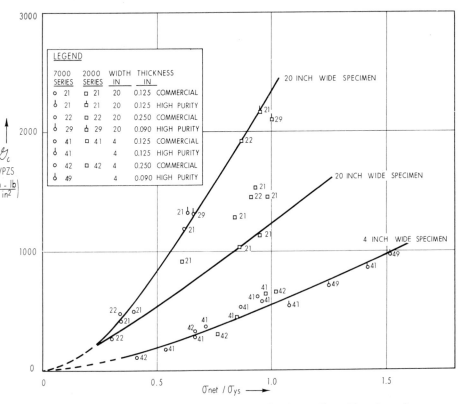

FIG. 54—*Fracture toughness values of sheet aluminum alloys (data from footnote 22).*

unjustifiably discredited by undiscriminating publication of the results of inadequate tests. In fairness to the source of Mr. Chu's Fig. 53, the authors of that compilation are careful to point out that some of the data are of dubious value.

With regard to Mr. Chu's Fig. 54, we make no attempt in our report to deal with K_c testing, as distinct from K_{Ic} testing, which would require another report of comparable size. As yet we do not have data on which to base such a report on K_c testing, and it would therefore be inappropriate to specifically discuss the data shown in Mr. Chu's Fig. 54. However, the authors have made a few general comments on mixed mode fracture testing in response to the discussion by Mr. Heyer.

With regard to fatigue cracking, we consider that it is better to state the limitations in terms of stress intensity rather than in terms of nominal stress, because the former retains the same meaning for different types of specimens while the latter does not. In our experience fatigue cracks formed in about 3000 cycles will tend to give high apparent K_{Ic} values when compared with fatigue cracks formed in about 30,000 cycles.

G. M. Orner and B. S. Lement[23]—The authors are to be congratulated for their up to date review of the important aspects of plane strain crack toughness testing. It is hoped that their paper will be published soon even though some of their recommendations are still tentative.

With respect to their discussion of "cracked Charpy specimens," we are in agreement that it is inaccurate to consider either an impact or slow bend W/A value as equal to $\mathcal{G}_{Ic}$ except possibly for very brittle alloys. However, we believe this mainly applies to W/A values obtained from specimens for which no attempt is made to prevent shear lip formation.

Attempts have been made to prevent shear lip formation by the "brittle boundary" technique. For example, slow bend tests by Hartbower and Orner[24] on brittle boundary specimens of 4340 steel indicated that the W/A value (as corrected using a specimen difference method) is independent of specimen thickness. Since Lement[25] failed to confirm this for 4335-V steel, further experiments along these lines would be necessary to better evaluate this approach.

On the other hand, the use of face notching for obtaining $\mathcal{G}_{Ic}$ from precracked slow bend tests is considered to be more promising. Hartbower and Orner[26] reported that W/A values obtained from slow bend tests of face notched 4340 steel, H-11 steel, and 7075-T651 aluminum specimens are independent of specimen thickness. In addition, Lement[27] found that face notching of 4335-V steel specimens gave W/A values that differed by about 10 per cent from $\mathcal{G}_{Ic}$, as determined by a circumferentially notched tension test. Although further work is necessary to establish the optimum face notching procedure, the advantage of this approach for obtaining $\mathcal{G}_{Ic}$ values in a simple fashion should not be overlooked.

[23] Man Labs, Inc., Cambridge, Mass.

[24] C. E. Hartbower and G. M. Orner, "Metallurgical Variables Affecting Fracture Toughness in High Strength Sheet Alloys," *ASD-TDR-62-868*, Part I, October, 1962.

[25] B. S. Lement, K. Kreder, and H. Tushman, "Investigation of Fracture Toughness in High Strength Alloys," *ASD-TDR-62-868*, Part II, January, 1964.

[26] G. M. Orner and C. E. Hartbower, "Precracked Charpy Fracture Toughness Correlations," paper presented at ASTM Symposium on Fracture Testing and Applications, June, 1964.

[27] B. S. Lement, unpublished results.

Although we advocate the use of W/A values as obtained from regular specimens (that is, without the use of a brittle boundary or face notching) for the screening of alloys or treatments, we believe that such values are indicative of relative G_c levels rather than G_{Ic} levels. In general, slow bend W/A values have been found to correlate fairly well with G_c values as obtained from center notched tension tests of the same material and thickness. For example, Hartbower and Orner tested 0.080-in.-thick sheets of X200, 300M, and H11 steels tempered in the range of 500 to 900 F and found that the ratio of slow bend W/A to G_c, as determined by center notched tension tests of 3-in.-wide specimens, was 0.85 ± 0.15. It should be noted that the W/A concept is not limited to "cracked Charpy tests" but can be used for other types of tests in which the total energy to propagate an initial crack up to complete fracture is determined. For example, Kaufman[28] has shown for aluminum alloys that W/A values obtained by the Alcoa modified Kahn tear test are in close agreement with G_c values.

The importance of determining fracture toughness values by both slow bend and impact tests should be emphasized. Because of the occurrence of time-dependent reactions, such as phase transformations and strain aging during testing, the slow bend W/A values are usually lower than the impact W/A values. Thus, if a large variation in strain rate or crack speed is possible under service conditions, both the slow bend and impact W/A values may be significant. This applies to W/A tests conducted under either essentially plane strain or plane stress conditions.

With respect to the ratio of crack length to specimen width (a/W), the cracked Charpy specimens generally are made with a crack length-to-width ratio of about 0.25 rather than 0.5, as stated by the authors.

Messrs. Brown and Srawley—We welcome the comments by Messrs. Orner and Lement, and we share their desire that the use of precracked Charpy specimens should be thoroughly evaluated. The most important thing to bear in mind is that precracked Charpy specimens are small three-point bend specimens which are subject to the same considerations as are applied to all other specimens used for K_{Ic} testing. We realize that the usual ratio of crack length-to-width is 0.25, but consider that the usefulness of the precracked Charpy specimen for K_{Ic} testing would be somewhat improved if this ratio was increased to 0.5, as suggested in our paper. This would increase the limit of valid K_{Ic} measurement, according to our criterion, from $0.2\ \sigma_{YS}$ to $0.28\ \sigma_{YS}$.

As discussed in our report, face grooving (notching) disturbs the crack front stress field in a manner which depends on groove depth, contour, and sharpness and which is not well understood. The practical

[28] J. G. Kaufman and A. H. Knoll, "Kahn Type Tear Tests and Crack Toughness of Aluminum Alloy Sheets," *Materials Research & Standards*, Vol 4, No. 151, April, 1964.

effect of face grooving is to eliminate part or all of the slow crack propagation phase of the test and to truncate the test record at some stress intensity less than that reached with a specimen that has not been face grooved. There is no obvious reason, however, why this truncation should invariably occur at K_{Ic}. In fact, the level of truncation will depend upon the face groove dimensions. Since we do not know how to determine exactly the right dimensions for face grooves, their use could lead to results which, while appearing to be well-defined, were nevertheless inaccurate. Of the data cited by the discussers, the results for the 7075-T651 aluminum alloy are in agreement with other available data, but the results for the two steels are substantially higher than we would expect at the hardness levels reported.

Fatigue cracking of Charpy specimens is often completed in a few thousand cycles, and since the starting notch is not very sharp (root radius 0.01 in.), we consider that the stress intensity required must be unduly high. As discussed in our report, the result of a K_{Ic} test can be adversely affected if the fatigue cracking stress intensity is excessive. The fatigue stress intensity necessary for cracking Charpy specimens could be substantially lowered if a sharper and deeper starting notch were used.

We are very dubious about the usefulness of cracked Charpy specimens for estimating K_c (contrasted to K_{Ic}) for several reasons, one reason being the small size of the specimen. Even if we assume the excessively liberal limit condition that the formal plane stress plastic zone size should not exceed the usual crack length, 0.1 in., we find that the maximum valid K_c value that could be measured would be 0.56 σ_{YS}. This is much less than the equivalent of some of the W/A values that have been reported as correlating with $\mathcal{G}_c$ values from other tests. It is difficult to see, therefore, how such correlations could be rationalized on the basis of linear elastic fracture mechanics.

Aside from other considerations, it should be appreciated that, in general, W/A is not equal to $\mathcal{G}_c$. The necessary condition for these two quantities to be equal is that the crack extension resistance should be constant, equal to $\mathcal{G}_c$, throughout the entire course of crack propagation. It follows that the load would have to start to decrease as soon as the crack extended, and to continue to decrease according to the relation: $P^2 = 2B\mathcal{G}_c/(dC/da)$, where dC/da is the derivative of specimen compliance with respect to crack length. Thus, for $\mathcal{G}_c$ to be proportional to the total area under the load deflection curve, it would be necessary for this condition to be met in a test in which no crack extension preceded maximum load. This, of course, would be a $\mathcal{G}_{Ic}$ test rather than a $\mathcal{G}_c$ test.

The interpretation of a test record when appreciable crack extension precedes maximum load can be illustrated by reference to Fig. 55.

The curved part of the loading line from P_I to P_c corresponds to a stage of slow crack extension preceding maximum load. It is customary to take W/A as the whole area under the curve OP_IP_cQ divided by $B(w - a_I)$, where B and w are the specimen thickness and width, and a_I is the initial crack length. This area cannot be proportional to $\mathcal{G}_c$, since it includes the area OP_IP_cO which represents the energy contribution associated with stable crack extension during increase of the crack extension resistance from $\mathcal{G}_{Ic}$ to $\mathcal{G}_c$. If it should happen that the condition: $P^2 = 2B\mathcal{G}_c/(dC/da)$ is satisfied for the descending branch P_cQ, then $\mathcal{G}_c$ will actually be equal to W'/A', where W' is the shaded area OP_cQ, and A' is equal to $B(w - a_c)$, a_c being the crack length at the maximum load P_c corresponding to onset of unstable fracture.

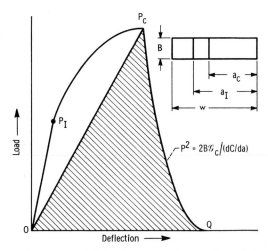

FIG. 55—*Schematic load-deflection record for crack-notch bend test.*

Without empirical evidence, however, there is no justification for assuming that the crack extension resistance will remain constant during unloading, and if it varies then there is no simple interpretation of either W'/A' or W/A. On the other hand, it is possible that in some instances W'/A' might be approximately equal to $\mathcal{G}_c$. Furthermore, W/A might fortuitously be approximately equal to W'/A', since W' is less than W and A' is less than A. It is possible in this way to account for some of the reported correlations between W/A and $\mathcal{G}_c$ in spite of the deficiencies of the assumption that W/A should be equal to $\mathcal{G}_c$. We see little value, however, in using the uncertain W/A approximation when $\mathcal{G}_c$ can be calculated more accurately in the usual way from the values of load and crack length at instability.

We agree that the sensitivity of fracture toughness to strain rate should be investigated when the application warrants. It would be desirable to conduct tests at a series of controlled strain rates, but the comparison of impact W/A values with slow bend values is no doubt a useful exploratory technique.

J. G. Kaufman[29]—I would like to call particular attention to the data in Figs. 10, 11, 13, 14, and 18, all of which show that when specimen size is deficient in some regard, either thickness, crack length, or ligament length, the "apparent" values of K_{Ic} calculated from the data are often higher than the true values of K_{Ic}. Though this point is mentioned in the paper, it needs to be stressed because there are many people who make the assumption undersized specimens always provide "lower bound" values and that the true value of K_{Ic} is higher than the calculated value. Recommendations for an increased amount of fracture toughness testing with subsize specimens have been made at times on this basis, but it is important that it be recognized that such testing may actually result in nonconservative values of the fracture parameters.

All of the discussion on the relative merits of specimens with part-through-cracks and through-cracks and the usefulness of one or the other must be tempered by the basic point made by the authors that the two types of specimens measure two different characteristics for materials which are not completely homogeneous and isotropic—and few metals actually are. With the part-through crack, the initial cracking is expected to be through the thickness, and any layering of the structure, either as a result of constituent stringers or simply the grain flow, will tend to make the resistance greater than that to the crack going along the length or width of the material as determined with a through-cracked specimen. In my opinion, this precludes the incorporation of a part-through-cracked specimen in a standard test method for the determination of the K_{Ic} values which might find their way indiscriminately into handbooks, after which they would be assumed to be useful in any type of design. I would go so far as to propose that the critical stress intensity factor obtained in tests of part-through-cracked-specimens have some unique designation, aside from K_{Ic}; the values may at times coincide with K_{Ic}, but in most cases, probably would not.

Messrs. Brown and Srawley—The authors agree with Mr. Kaufman in his emphasis on the point that testing subsize specimens may yield values of K_{Ic} that overestimate the capabilities of the material in the presence of flaws larger than those used in the specimen. We also agree that most materials are not isotropic regarding their fracture characteristics. For this reason it is important to evaluate the crack toughness in all directions that would be expected to carry substantial stresses in service.

R. H. Heyer,[30]—This paper will be invaluable in preparing the long

---

[29] Research Laboratories, Aluminum Company of America, New Kensington, Pa.

[30] Research Center, Armco Steel Corp., Middletown, Ohio.

awaited recommended practice, and its authors should be decorated in some fitting manner.

We found the new simplified procedure for determining allowable deviation from linearity and minimum popin displacement much more satisfactory than the previous one. Specimen size requirements, fortunately, can be specified with more assurance as the suggested procedures are used to obtain data for additional materials. The paper should generate considerable interest in this area.

If the proposed thickness requirements are confirmed, the range of application of valid K_{Ic} testing will be quite restrictive, and the need for mixed mode fracture toughness criteria remains.

While parameters which are independent of thickness are highly desirable, they may be unattainable for materials not amenable to K_{Ic} testing, and serious consideration may have to be given to parameters applicable within limited thickness ranges. In the recently published proposed recommended practice for sharp-notch strength, for example, comparisons must be based on specimens having the same nominal thickness. The only alternative at present to the use of sharp-notch strength is to continue using Charpy and other transition temperature based tests.

The statement about significance of invalid K_{Ic} tests is likely to be controversial. It can be argued that obtaining an invalid K_{Ic} due to inadequate specimen size is not an assurance that the material is tough enough for the application, even though certain test conditions, including thickness, match service conditions. Specifically, dynamic loading in service may be a condition not matched by the K_{Ic} test.

Messrs. Brown and Srawley—We agree with Mr. Heyer that the need for mixed mode fracture toughness criteria still remains. It was the intended purposes of K_c testing to provide such criteria, and measurement of K_c first appeared to be a relatively straightforward procedure. However, we now realize that the mechanics of mixed mode fracturing is indeed a complex problem. There are two basic difficulties: (1) relatively large amounts of crack tip plastic flow accompany crack propagation, and (2) the point of unstable fracture is difficult to establish in terms of a "critical" crack length and load. The relatively large amount of plastic flow accompanying crack propagation requires the use of correspondingly large specimens. Even if the specimens are sufficiently large to permit use of elastic fracture mechanics, and the instrumentation sufficiently sophisticated to permit determination of a critical crack length, the resulting K_c values are unlikely to be independent of crack length and width. Additional discussion of the problems associated with K_c testing is given in Refs 10 and 28 of the paper.

From the foregoing it is clear that we consider mixed mode elastic fracture mechanics as an important subject for further research rather than a useful engineering tool. A substantial reduction in specimen size probably will require a fracture mechanics based on the three-dimensional plastic stress and strain distribution in cracked bodies. This is certainly a formidable problem; however, there is reason to believe that useful approximations are possible providing the correct models are chosen.

In the meantime the evaluation of the fracture properties of tough low strength alloys must be by means of empirical tests. However, we see no way of avoiding the testing of materials in full service thickness using properly designed fatigue cracked specimens. This will require a number of arbitrary decisions concerning both specimen design and data interpretation. However, these can be made in a way that leads to conservative results. For example, in the case of heavy sections, it might be required that a center crack specimen of full thickness with a crack length, say twice the thickness, fails at a net stress at least equal to the yield strength. With some experience a corresponding test using an instrumented bend specimen might be developed. Tests on thin sections of high toughness alloys constitute less of a problem in material and load requirement. The aircraft industry regularly establishes the crack tolerance of sheet alloys by tests on wide panels to directly establish the relation between crack length and failure stress. In this connection, determination of nominal K_c values (based on the initial crack lengths) may be useful. While these are not independent of specimen dimensions, they are considerably less dependent on crack length and specimen width than the gross or net fracture stress.

The use of small specimens such as the Charpy V to screen alloys regarding their fracture characteristics in heavy sections must be approached with considerable caution. This is a useful procedure only when a background of experience shows that the data desired from the small specimens do correlate with the fracture behavior in heavy sections. Such correlations have been established by Pellini and his co-workers for ship steels; however, the extent of their usefulness in the evaluation of more complex alloys has yet to be established.

P. N. Randall[31]—The test results to be discussed were part of a recent study of the surface-cracked specimen sponsored by the Air Force Materials Laboratory.[32] One objective of that study was to measure the effects of crack size and shape on flaw severity, that is, on the stress at fracture in specimens containing surface cracks. The results apply to the problem of estimating the severity of natural flaws in hardware and also to the problem of devising standard tests for the measurement of fracture toughness.

From linear, elastic fracture mechanics come formulas that estab-

---

[31] TRW Systems, Redondo Beach, Calif.

[32] P. N. Randall, "Severity of Natural Flaws as Fracture Origins, and a Study of the Surface-Cracked Specimen," *AFML-TR-66-204*, August, 1966.

lish what function of flaw geometry should characterize its "size" or severity. Only certain cases have been worked out—all of them for sharp cracks such as fatigue cracks. For the surface-cracked specimen, the relationship of failure stress to flaw geometry, developed by Irwin,[33] is as follows:

$$\sigma = 0.515 \, K_{Ic}/\sqrt{a/Q} \dots \dots \dots (8).$$

where:

σ = stress on gross section, ksi,

a/Q = normalized crack depth, in., and

K_{Ic} = stress intensity factor at onset of unstable, plane-strain fracturing, ksi$\sqrt{\text{in.}}$

This expression shows the severity of a semiellipitical crack to be characterized by the length of its semiminor axis, a, which is usually the crack depth, modified by a factor Q. The function Q depends primarily on the ratio of crack depth-to-length and secondarily on a correction term for plastic strains near the crack boundary. Neglecting the latter, Q ranges in value from 1.00 for long, shallow cracks to 2.46 for semicircular cracks.

To provide a basis for comparison in later studies of flaw severity, Task I in the program was to measure the fracture toughness of each material using the conventional surface-cracked specimen. Several sizes of cracks were used, ranging from the largest permitted by current rules —crack depth equal to one half the specimen thickness and crack length equal to one third the width—to the smallest crack that produced failure at a stress less than the yield strength. All were "normal" cracks, grown in bending fatigue from a point source.

The purpose of Task II was to measure the effects of crack shape. First to be tested were semielliptical cracks that were long and shallow and those that were short and deep for comparison with those of normal proportions. In addition, some nonelliptical cracks were tested—those having crack front curvatures that differed from that of a semielliptical crack of the same depth and length.

Results are discussed in terms of how well the standard expression for K_{Ic}, when applied to these shapes, gave agreement with the values from normal cracks. Corrections or modifications to the standard expression were also tried. The shape correction was based on actual crack front curvature measurements. The effect of the back-face free surface on stress intensity factor was evaluated, using the analytical work of others. The net section effect, which arises when crack area is a significant part of the gross, was also evaluated. Measurements of

---

[33] G. R. Irwin, "Crack Extension Force for a Part-Through Crack in A Plate," *Journal of Applied Mechanics* (*Transactions*, Am. Society Mechanical Engrs.), December, 1962, pp. 651–654.

crack opening displacement versus load were recorded during each test to look for popin and evidence of plastic strain.

Experimental

Materials

A low-alloy steel and a titanium alloy were tested, each at two strength levels. The higher yield strength level (designated *"high"*) was chosen to represent material of such limited ductility that the data could be treated in terms of linear elastic fracture mechanics with some confidence. The level chosen was at or slightly above the currently accepted maximum for carefully made hardware. The lower yield strength level (designated *"low"*) was chosen to be near the conventional strength for these materials when used in the heat-treated condition; hence, their fracture toughness should be fairly high. The plastic zone at the crack tip should be of significant size; consequently, more caution should be required in the use of fracture mechanics in interpretation of the data.

The D6-AC material was purchased as a ring forging, 62 in. diameter by 26 in. wide by 0.93 in. thick—a spinning preform for Minuteman first stage cases. It was furnished in the rough machined condition, following heat treatment that consisted of normalizing at 1700 F, followed by a double temper at 1300 F. The specimens (5 in. long) were oriented circumferentially. This was vacuum arc remelted material. The chemistry certified by the melter and forge shop, Standard Steel Div. of the Baldwin Lima Hamilton Corp., was as follows: (all values are weight per cent) C 0.45, Si 0.24, P 0.007, Mn 0.60, S 0.006, Ni 0.52, Cr 1.11, Mo 0.99, and V 0.13.

Heat treatment of the D6-AC specimens, performed after finish machining, was as follows: austenitize 45 min at 1650 F in an argon atmosphere, quench in salt at 400 F, cool in air to below 100 F, return immediately to salt bath for snap draw at 400 F for 1 hr, air cool and clean off the salt. Tempering was done at one of two temperatures, for a period of 4 hr with the following results.

	D6-AC *High*	D6-AC *Low*
Tempering temperature	1050 F	550 F
Tempering atmosphere	argon	air
Ultimate strength, ksi	290	230
	288	229
Average	289	230
Yield strength (0.2% offset), ksi	252	212
	246	211
Average	249	212
Hardness, R_c	52 to 53	47 to 48

The Ti-6Al-4V material used for the *"low"* strength designation was purchased as $\frac{3}{4}$-in. plate, in the annealed condition. Chemistry certified by the mill, Republic Steel Corp., was as follows: Al 5.83, V 3.78, Fe 0.16, C 0.024, N_2 0.022, and H_2 0.008. Oxygen content, measured during unsuccessful efforts to achieve high yield strength, was 0.09 per cent. The specimen length was oriented in the rolling direction.

The Ti-6Al-4V material used for the *"high"* strength designation was purchased as 2-in.-diameter bar (in the annealed condition) from Titanium Metals Corp., who certified its chemical composition to be as follows: Al 6.2, V 4.2, Fe 0.15, C 0.025, N 0.013, H 0.0074, and Oxygen 0.195. Pairs of specimens were cut from each 5-in. length of bar.

Heat treatment of the Ti-6Al-4V material was carried out on rough-machined specimens, 0.35 in. thick. Results were as follows:

	Ti-6Al-4V *High*	Ti-6Al-4V *Low*
Solution temperature (1 hr in argon)......	1775 F	1750 F
Quench (less than 6 sec delay)............	water at 40 F	water at 80 F
Aging temperature (4 hr duration)........	925 F	1000 F
Ultimate strength, ksi....................	175	163
	174	162
Average...........................	174	162
Yield strength, ksi.......................	161	155
	159	153
Average...........................	160	154
Hardness, R_c...........................	44.5 to 45.5	41 to 42

Specimen Preparation

One specimen geometry—the button-head flat tension specimen shown in Fig. 56—was used for the smooth tensions as well as the surface-cracked ones. This configuration was chosen for its economy of material. When circumstances call for small specimens machined from thick plate or bar, thickness must be reduced in the gage section anyway, so it is economical of specimen material and shop time to grip the specimen in the fillets, instead of using pin connections.

In some cases, the button-head had to be reduced to 0.65 in. wide. To make sure the button heads would not pull off, a pair of smaller specimens with button heads that were just two times the gage thickness were tested. They did not fail at the fillet, but there were indications of plastic flow.

Requirements of convenience in finish machining resulted in the W/B ratio of 5.6. This is believed to be close enough to the arbitrary limit of

6.0 called out in footnote[34] to satisfy the purposes of this test. The width was limited to 1.4 in., because standard 1-in. diameter end mills are only 1.50 in. long. Larger end mills would force the use of larger test fixtures and longer specimens.

Cracking Procedures

Task I involved basic tests of specimens containing semielliptical cracks of normal proportions, which are defined as those that occur

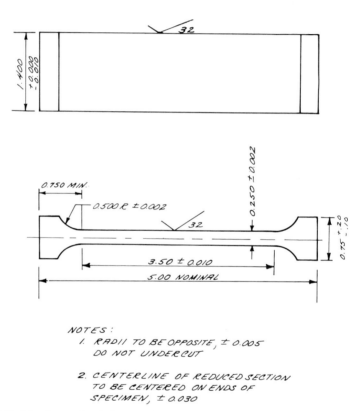

FIG. 56—*Button-head flat tensile and surface-cracked specimen. Note: all dimensions are in inches.*

when grown in cantilever bending fatigue from a point source—an origin that is small in relation to the final crack size. For these "normal" cracks, the origin was usually an arc burn, actually an indentation formed by a sharp, tungsten-tipped welding electrode at low power. For D6-AC *low*, however, crack starters made by ultrasonic machining

---

[34] P. N. Randall and R. P. Felgar, "Part-Through Crack Test—Relation to Solid Propellant Rocket Cases," *Journal of Basic Engineering* (*Transactions*, Am. Society Mechanical Engrs.), December, 1964, pp. 685–692.

were substituted for those made by arc burns because the arc burn was not always severe enough to start the fatigue crack quickly. Slots 0.100 in. long by 0.020 in. deep by 0.010 in. wide were used. An alternate approach was to raise the bending stress, but then sometimes the fatigue crack grew too rapidly, following its initiation, and the final length was hard to control. Furthermore, the fatigue crack surface was found to be rough and so nearly indistinguishable from that of the tensile fracture that the crack dimensions were difficult to measure.

The stress cycle imposed was always one of 0-to-tension. The maximum stress levels that were finally evolved were: for the D6-AC (both *high* and *low*), 125 ksi until the crack appeared well started, then 100 ksi to completion; for the Ti-6Al-4V (both *high* and *low*), 100 ksi, then 75 ksi. Number of cycles to complete the crack ranged from 10,000 to 20,000 total with about half that number required to produce the first observable crack.

Equipment used for the bending fatigue cracking was a Tatnall-Krause Plate Fatigue machine, modified as shown in Fig. 57. The drive motor had been changed to one of variable speed to facilitate observation and control of crack growth. Normal running speed was about 600 rpm; above that, vibration was too severe. Cracks were grown to the chosen length, measured with the filar eyepiece of the microscope with the speed reduced to about 60 rpm.

For Task II, abnormal crack shapes, special effort was required to avoid growing cracks of normal proportions (those originating at a point source). Thus, for example, although a long, shallow slot was used for a crack starter to grow a long, shallow fatigue crack, it often happened that another originated. The result was a crack of nearly normal proportions. Techniques worked out for getting multiple fatigue crack origins were as follows:

1. Use as sharp a starter notch as possible. The limit in our case was determined by the thickness of the ultrasonic cutting tool that would not buckle—0.010-in. shim stock for most cases. A series of arc burns made with a tungsten-tipped etching point was used occasionally to supplement the machined slot.

2. Begin the cracking process at a high stress level, and drop to a lower one after several crack origins are seen.

3. Vary the point of support, placing it beneath the region where a crack origin is desired. This was surprisingly effective in specimens of this thickness.

The long, shallow cracks were grown in bending fatigue, using the equipment described above. Short, deep cracks were grown in axial fatigue, using the equipment illustrated in Fig. 58. A closed-loop hydraulic system (made by Research Inc.), controlling off the load cell, provided a cyclic fatigue load from the hydraulic cylinder. The usual stress cycle was 10 to 75 ksi, tension-to-tension at a frequency of 10

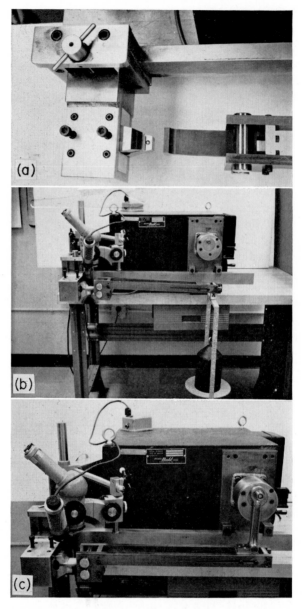

FIG. 57—*Modified Tatnall-Krouse plate fatigue machine used to produce surface cracks, (a) prior to assembly, (b) during dead weight calibration to set the throw of the eccentric, and (c) ready for operation.*

FIG. 58—*Hydraulic tester used as an axial fatigue machine to grow short, deep cracks.*

FIG. 59—*Typical crack sizes and shapes tested. "Normal cracks" are in the middle column.*

to 12 cps. Typical results of these efforts are shown in Fig. 59. Note the shapes and sizes of the ultrasonic slots relative to those of the fatigue cracks.

Twin-Crack Specimen

The twin-crack specimen, used throughout this part of the program, was made simply by growing two cracks of identical size (hopefully) in each specimen. To avoid interaction of their stress fields, they were placed on opposite faces of the specimen, spaced 1 in. apart axially, as illustrated in Fig. 60.

The purpose of the twin-crack specimen was to obtain visual information about crack growth prior to maximum load. The crack that did

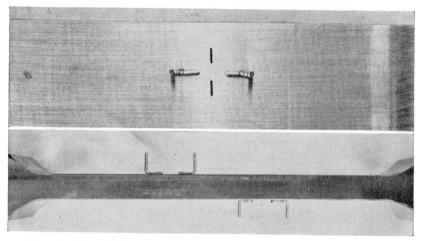

FIG. 60—*Twin-crack specimen, showing axial displacement of cracks on opposite faces. The spot-welded wires support the COD gage points.*

not become the fracture origin, called the "secondary" crack, was heat stained, cooled in liquid nitrogen, and broken open to reveal the extent of slow growth. This was of particular interest in the studies of crack shape, to see if crack growth prior to maximum load had altered the shape of the fatigue crack. Also, interpretation of the crack opening displacement record for the secondary crack was made easier by the direct information about slow growth.

Figure 61 illustrates the slow growth of a secondary crack in a low-strength D6-AC specimen. Note that the heat stain extends only part way across the region between the edge of the fatigue crack and the mark that bounds the slow grown crack. The mark is too distinct to ignore, and there is no other explanation for its presence there; hence, the conclusion is that heat staining does not necessarily reveal all the slow growth. Elastic recovery of the surrounding metal apparently closes the crack too tightly to admit air during heat staining.

Test Fixtures and Procedures

A general view of the test setup is shown in Fig. 62. At the upper end of the string is the load cell, the output of which drives the vertical axis of the recorder of crack opening displacement. Beneath the load cell a coupling can be seen, then the specimen holders that carry the adjustable spherical seats, the specimen between them, the crack-opening displacement gages suspended from the upper cross head, and finally the lower cross head of the testing machine.

FIG. 61—*Slow growth of secondary crack in low-strength D6-AC steel. The first beach mark below the ultrasonic slot occurred when the fatigue stress level was reduced, the next is the fatigue crack front. The narrow, dark border is heat-stained slow growth. The bright border is also slow growth, bounded by a region in shadow.*

Details of the ball seat and the gripping arrangements are shown in Fig. 63. One-inch hardened pins that bear in the fillets of the button head support the specimen. They are readily pushed to one end to admit the specimen. The center of the ball seat was placed at the button head, so that its rotation could accommodate any lack of oppositeness of the fillets.

The general requirement of axial loading in tension testing is somewhat complex in the case of the surface-cracked specimen because its net section is eccentric to the gross section. Furthermore, the studies of crack shape and size planned for this program are sensitive to this situation, because these variables affect the eccentricity of the net section; yet, we want to minimize the resulting effect on strength, relative to the effects of crack shape and size *per se*. It appeared that the assumptions made in analysis would be met best by attempting to produce uniform stress across the thickness of the specimen near the edges, where the stress field of the crack is insignificant. To do so, strains were compared on the front and back surfaces of the specimen near one edge by means of the axiality indicator illustrated in Fig. 64. Its indication is a measure of bending strain in a ½-in. gage length centered on the crack. While the

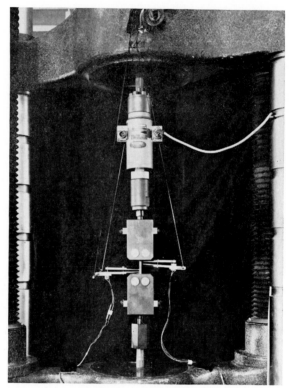

FIG. 62—*Test setup in the Baldwin hydraulic testing machine.*

uniform strain in the specimen is included, its magnitude is known to the operator (it is proportional to the load), and it is relatively small because the bending strain is magnified 16 times and the uniform strain is not. It was found possible to insure that the bending strain did not exceed 2 per cent of the average strain at these loads. The gage was removed prior to test.

Crack opening displacement was measured by means of specially-built extensometers, working on a gage length approximately equal to the crack length in each case. Primary intended use of the records of load versus crack opening was as an indicator of popin or of slow crack growth. In past published work it has generally been assumed that the

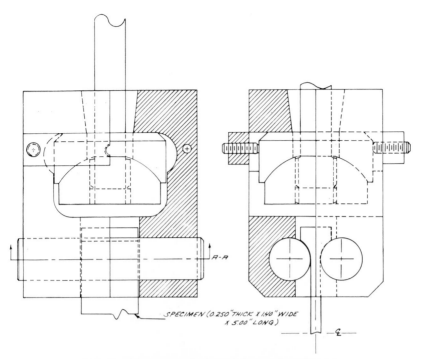

SPECIMEN (0.250" THICK X 1.140" WIDE X 5.00" LONG)

FIG. 63—*Two sectional views of the specimen holder.*

FIG. 64—*Axiality gage in position on the specimen.*

slow growth of part-through cracks was negligible, but proof of this was necessary if the original crack size was to be used in calculations. For the cracks of irregular shape the record of crack opening displacement was watched for indications that the crack front had popped forward to a more stable shape—one of sharper curvature—prior to maximum load.

Figure 65 shows the crack-opening displacement gage, suspended against the cracked face of the specimen with the tips of the gage inserted between the wire studs to permit the gage to fall free without

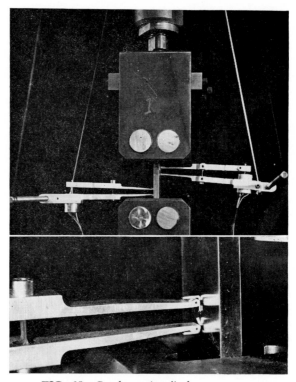

FIG. 65—*Crack-opening displacement gages.*

suffering a large acceleration when the specimen broke. The studs were attached to the specimen by spot welds, spaced one crack length apart, spanning the crack on both faces of the specimen. The differential transformer drove the horizontal axis of the recorder. Sensitivity of the transducer-recorder system was sufficient to permit a magnification ratio of 1000.

Test Results for Semielliptical Cracks

Characteristics of "Normal" Cracks

If the surface-cracked specimen is to be used for standardized fracture toughness tests, the cracks would almost certainly be grown in bending fatigue from a point source, because this technique is the least expensive and the one most widely used today. Consequently, the data obtained from specimens of all four materials were examined to learn the characteristics of "normal" cracks.

The shape of normal cracks was found to be somewhat dependent on their size and on the material toughness. As illustrated in Fig. 66, the ratio, crack depth/length, ranges from almost 0.500 (a semicircle) for the smallest cracks, to 0.280 for cracks whose depth was one half the

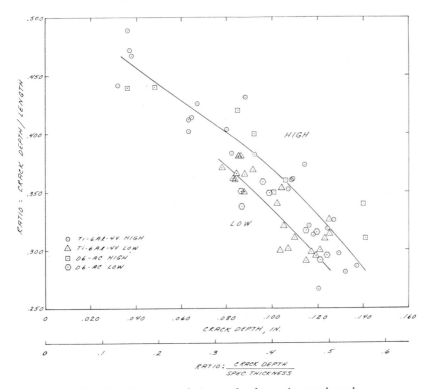

FIG. 66—*Effect of crack size on the shape of normal cracks.*

specimen thickness. This is perhaps not surprising, because the bottom of the crack must penetrate a region of lower nominal stress as it grows. Deep cracks in the *low* material were longer than those in the *high*. Apparently, low toughness permits the cracks to penetrate into the low stress region near midthickness more readily.

As stated in the introduction, the quantity normally used to characterize the severity of semielliptical cracks is a/Q. Pending the derivation given in later discussion, it is sufficient to show here how Q is obtained from the nomograph, Fig. 67, that is commonly used in data reduction. It is primarily a function of a/c, the ratio of lengths of the axes of the ellipse. The ordinate of the graph was made $a/2c$, because

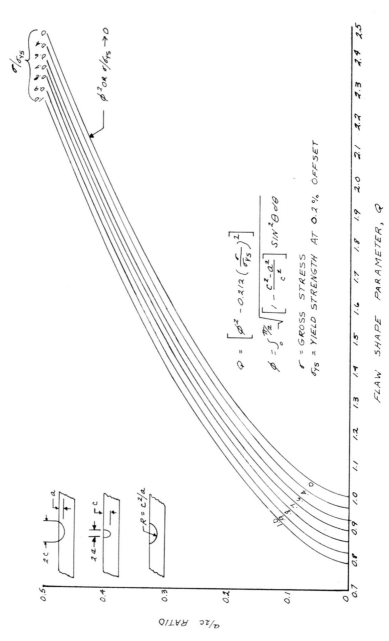

FIG. 67—*Flaw-shape parameter curves for surface cracks.*

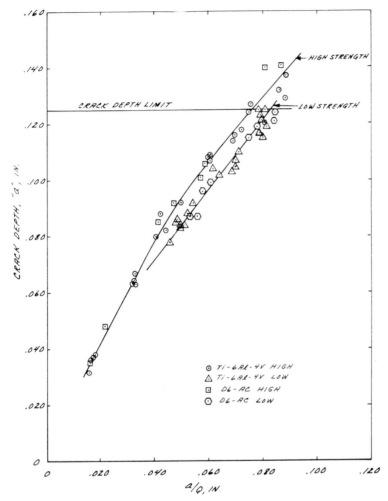

FIG. 68—*Relationship of normalized crack depth to crack depth, for all normal cracks.*

this is the ratio of depth-to-length for most cracks. For cracks that are deeper, relative to their length than a semicircle ($a/2c > 0.500$), the terms have a different meaning, as shown in the inset of the figure.

The secondary term in the function for Q represents an effective increase in crack depth to include the radius of the plastic zone, as estimated from the ratio of the gross stress to the yield strength. The term is evaluated by selecting the proper curve from the family.

Figure 68 illustrates the point that a/Q is not quite a linear function of a for these normal cracks, because their shape varies with size. The difference in shape between *high* and *low* materials has an effect on this function also. The crack depth limit shown in the figure—one half the specimen thickness—is that commonly given in statements of recommended practice.

Since crack area has been considered an empirical measure of crack severity, by the writer[34] and others, a correlation of crack area with

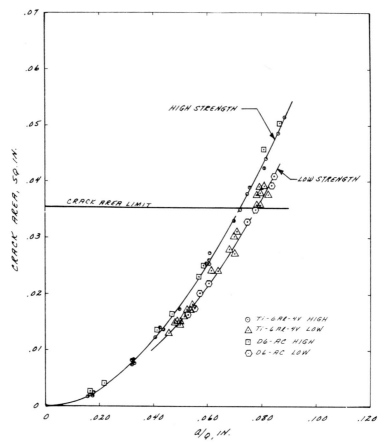

FIG. 69—*Relationship of crack area to normalized crack depth for all normal cracks.*

a/Q for normal cracks is given in Fig. 69. The relationship looks parabolic and would be exactly so if crack shape were constant with size. Again the data for *high* and *low* materials fall on separate curves. The crack area limit shown—10 per cent of the gross area—is again a requirement proposed as a recommended practice.

The following part of the program being a study of crack shape, a natural question arose, "Are the normal-shaped cracks really semi-elliptical?" To answer this, curvature measurements were made, using a

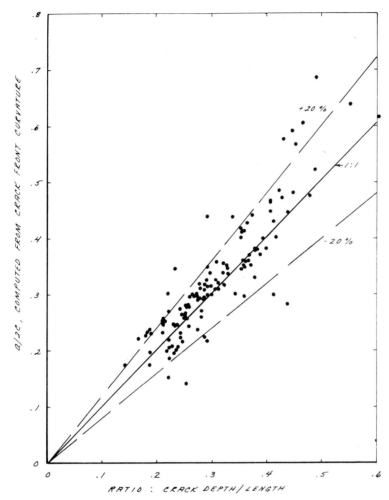

FIG. 70—*Comparison of actual ratio of crack depth to length of all normal cracks with the value computed from crack front curvature measurements, assuming the shape is semielliptical.*

set of elliptical templates and a comparator with magnification of 10X or 20X, depending on crack size. The templates were matched to the crack front curvature over about the middle third of the crack length. Repeatability of the radius of curvature measurement was about ±10 per cent on a well-defined crack. At the end of the minor axis of an ellipse $R = c^2/a$; hence,

$$\frac{a}{2c} = \frac{1}{2}\sqrt{\frac{a}{R}}$$

Figure 70 plots the comparison of $a/2c$ values obtained in this way

with those from direct measurement. The evidence is quite clear that
these normal cracks are semielliptical, at least near midlength, which
is probably where it matters. Stated another way, their curvature near
midlength was approximately that of a semiellipse whose semiminor
axis was crack depth and whose major axis was crack length.

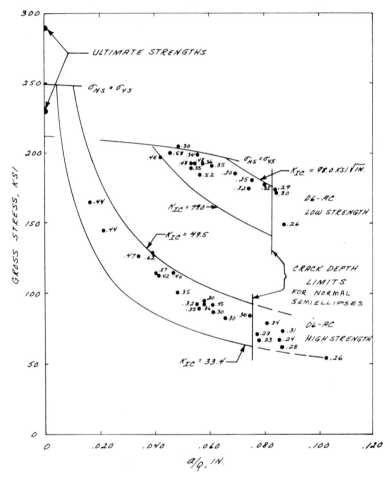

FIG. 71—*Relationship of stress to flaw size for D6-AC at both strength levels.
Beside each data point is the ratio: crack depth/length. Date are for specimens
having semielliptical cracks.*

Fracture Toughness of the Four Materials

The original test plan envisioned that for the normal cracks, shape
would remain nearly constant with size, so the K_{Ic} values computed
from those tests would provide the baseline for later studies of crack
shape. Since this did not prove to be the case, the data for all semielliptical cracks will be presented together. The actual decision as to
what was semielliptical was based on a comparison of K_{Ic} values com-

puted from the results of the two methods for obtaining $a/2c$. If they agreed within 5 per cent, the measured value was used, and the datum point was put in the semielliptical group.

The effect of flaw severity as measured by a/Q on gross stress at maximum load for both strength levels of the D6-AC steel is shown in Fig. 71. Clearly the terms *high* and *low* do not refer to strength in the presence of these flaws—they refer only to the strength of smooth specimens. The data for each strength level are bounded above and below by the inverse square root relationship

$$\sigma = 0.515 \ K_{\text{Ic}} / \sqrt{a/Q}$$

using the maximum and minimum values of K_{Ic} for the data that are enclosed. The line representing the yield stress limitation, labeled $\sigma_{\text{NS}} = \sigma_{\text{YS}}$, droops down from the yield strength value at large crack sizes, because the limitation is on the net stress not the gross. To plot this limit line, the correlation of crack area to a/Q given in Fig. 69 was used; hence, it is somewhat approximate. At the right, the limit line was determined by the requirement that crack depth not exceed one half the specimen thickness, using the correlation of crack depth to a/Q given in Fig. 68.

The first observation to be made concerns the fit of the data to the prediction of fracture mechanics. The total spread is ± 19 per cent for D6-AC *high* and ± 11 per cent for D6-AC *low*. A closer look at the data shows that this is not all scatter, part of it is a trend in the data. That for D6-AC *high* trend downward with crack size faster than the expression for K_{Ic} predicts, and that for D6-AC *low* trend downward very gradually—less than the K_{Ic} predicts. A study of this effect in terms of individual K_{Ic} values from each test will be discussed below.

The second observation to be made about the data in Fig. 71 concerns the effect of crack shape, which is noted beside each datum point. If there is any tendency for the data from cracks of a certain shape to be segregated, they are masked by other factors.

In parallel fashion, the effect of flaw severity, as measured by a/Q, on gross stress for both Ti-6Al-4V *high* and *low* is shown in Fig. 72. The spread in K_{Ic} values was ± 15 per cent, for Ti-6Al-4V *high* and ± 13 per cent for the *low*. Again, part of this is caused by trends much like those observed for the D6-AC.

The effect of crack shape, again, is not apparent. Data points for $a/2c$ ratios in the range of 0.20 are intermingled with those of 0.50. The conclusion seems to be that, within the range of $a/2c$ ratios tested in these specimens, all of which contained semielliptical cracks, the effect of crack shape was adequately accounted for by the function, Q.

The effect of crack size does not appear to be adequately treated by the term, a/Q. This can be seen more directly in Fig. 73, in which K_{Ic}

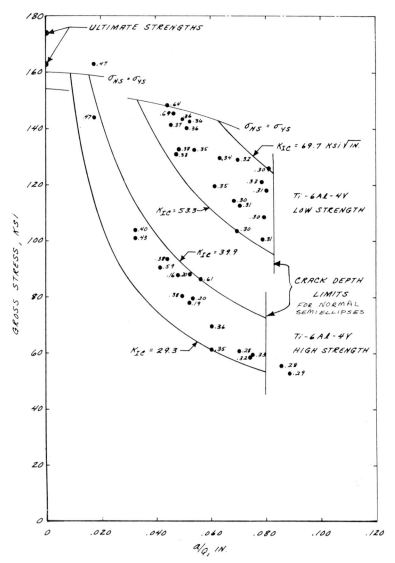

FIG. 72—*Relationship of stress to flaw size for Ti-6Al-4V at both strength levels. All data are for semielliptical cracks.*

values from individual specimens are plotted as a function of a/Q. Both materials, when heat treated to the *high* condition, with accompanying low toughness, show a downward trend in K_{Ic} with increasing crack size. In the tough condition, however, both Ti-6Al-4V *low* and D6-AC *low* show an increase in K_{Ic} with increasing crack size. To explain these opposite trends requires consideration of other variables that change when a/Q increases. Two, in particular, are: (1) the proximity of the crack tip to the back face, and (2) the ratio of net stress to

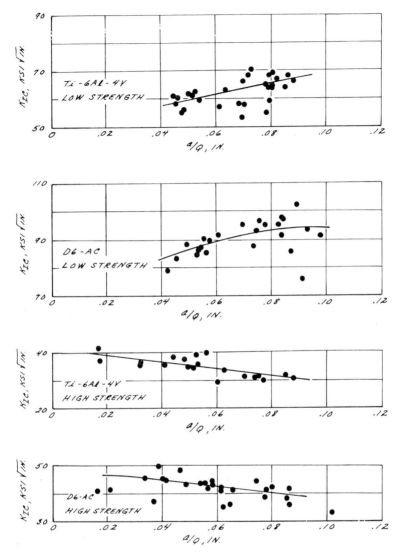

FIG. 73—*Effect of crack size on K_{Ic}, conventional, for all four materials, for the specimens having semielliptical cracks.*

gross. Both increase when crack size increases. Before examining these factors in detail it is appropriate to first review the derivation of the expression for K_{Ic}.

Stress Intensity Factor, K_{IC} for Surface-Cracked Specimens—Review of Derivation

Stress intensity factor may be defined in the following way. For a sharp crack, one having zero root radius, the stress a short distance r

ahead of the crack tip is porportional to $1/\sqrt{2\pi r}$. That proportionality factor is called the "stress intensity factor." It has the general form: nominal stress times the square root of crack depth modified where necessary by some function of crack shape.

The physical basis for the use of stress intensity factor in studies of the measurement of crack severity rests on a general belief that fracture occurs when the stress level in a "sufficiently large volume" of material near the crack tip exceeds a critical value. This concept has been discussed by Weiss and Yukawa,[35] who credit it to Ludwik et al. The question, "what constitutes a sufficiently large volume?" has no neat answer at present. The $1/\sqrt{2\pi r}$ term in the stress analysis predicts infinite stress at the crack tip at any nominal stress level above zero (which prevents the simple use of a stress concentration factor instead of a stress intensity factor). This means that small cracks produce the same range of stress levels as large ones, that is, both produce stresses ranging downward from infinite at the crack tip to the nominal stress at some distance away from the tip. Thus, the concept of a "sufficiently large volume" is also necessary to an understanding of the effect of crack size on fracture stress.

Moreover, a realistic picture of the situation at the crack tip, for metals, requires an understanding of the effects of plastic flow there. The plastic zone probably extends beyond the critical volume of metal in which fracture initiation takes place. Overlying all these questions is that concerning whether the conditions governing crack initiation are the same as those governing crack propagation. Use of the stress intensity factor to predict fracture implies that they are—that when the stress levels within the critical volume of metal reach the value required to initiate a crack, the stored elastic energy that is available to propagate the crack is sufficient to do so.

The objective of the following derivation is to obtain a relationship between nominal stress, the dimensions of the surface crack in a plate, and the stress intensity factor. This is an exercise in theory of elasticity, unrelated as yet to fracture toughness. Stress intensity factor is simply the multiplier of $1/\sqrt{2\pi r}$ in the expression for stresses near the tip of a sharp crack. Steps in the analysis are given in tabular form to make it easier to flag the assumptions involved in each step.

Review of Irwin's Analysis

Step 1 in Analysis:

Irwin's starting point[33] was the Green-Sneddon solution[36] for a complete ellipse, a flat ellipse with a sharp crack front, embedded in an

---

[35] V. Weiss and S. Yukawa, "Critical Appraisal of Fracture Mechanics," *Fracture Toughness Testing and Its Applications, ASTM STP 381*, Am. Soc. Testing Mats., 1965.

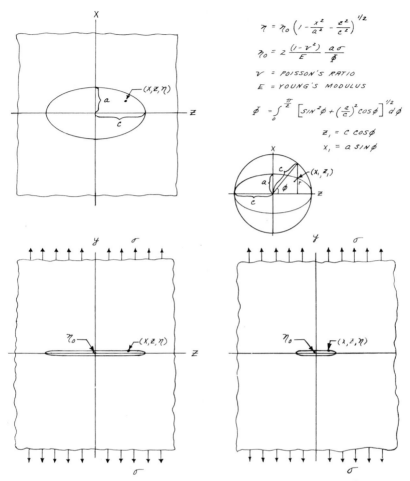

FIG. 74—*Three views of the shape assumed by a flat, elliptical crack in an infinite body when subjected to a uniaxial stress, σ, normal to the plane.*

infinite body, subjected to uniaxial tension normal to the plane of the crack, as illustrated in Fig. 74.

The expressions for stresses around the crack were not given explicitly and are not easily obtained. However, it was shown that the flat ellipse becomes an ellipsoid under stress, where

$$\eta = \eta_0 \left(1 - \frac{x^2}{a^2} - \frac{z^2}{c^2} \right)^{1/2}$$

Furthermore, η_0, the maximum displacement of one crack surface from its unstressed position, was related to stress and crack dimensions by:

[36] A. E. Green and I. N. Sneddon, "The Distribution of Stress in the Neighborhood of a Flat Elliptical Crack in an Elastic Solid," *Proceedings*, Cambridge Philosophical Soc., Vol 46, 1950, pp. 159–164.

$$\eta_0 = \frac{2(1 - \nu^2)}{E} \frac{a\sigma}{\Phi}$$

Terms are defined in Fig. 74.

(*Assumptions*—None, except those commonly assumed in the theory of elasticity.)

Step 2 in Analysis:

Knowing the shape of the opened elliptical crack in terms of its dimensions and the stress, Irwin next made use of a Westergaard solution[37] that relates crack opening displacement to stress intensity factor near a straight crack front. The case Westergaard solved was: a through crack in a body in a condition of plane strain, a "flat" crack with sharp, straight crack fronts, body subjected to equal biaxial tension. Stress was related to crack opening displacement near the crack front by:

$$\eta = \frac{2(1 - \nu^2)}{E} (2r)^{1/2} K$$

$$K = \sigma \sqrt{a}$$

Terms are defined in Fig. 75.

In recent analytical work, a term, $(\pi)^{1/2}$, enters in:

$$\eta = \frac{2(1 - \nu^2)}{E} \left(\frac{2r}{\pi}\right)^{1/2} K$$

$$K = \sigma \sqrt{\pi a}$$

While the relationship of η to σ, a, r, and E is obviously not affected, the comparison of K values for cracks of several geometries requires consistency, and the $\sqrt{\pi}$ term will be included.

(*Assumptions*—The relationship of stress intensity factor, K, to crack opening displacement η, is not affected by (*a*) crack front curvature (*b*) variation of η along the crack front, or (*c*) the presence of biaxial tension.

In Westergaard's work, none except those commonly assumed in the theory of elasticity.

The term r is small relative to a.)

Step 3 in Analysis:

Before substituting η from Westergaard for η from Green and Sneddon, it was necessary to rewrite the latter in terms of the angle ϕ and a distance r, measured inward, normal to the crack front. (See Fig. 74.) Irwin found:

[37] H. M. Westergaard, "Bearing Pressures and Cracks," *Journal of Applied Mechanics*, June, 1939, pp. A-49 to A-53.

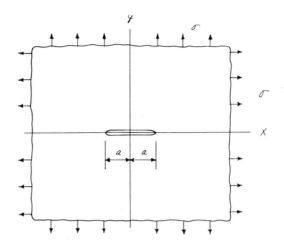

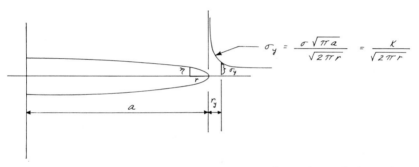

FIG. 75—*Elliptical shape assumed by a flat, straight crack in a body in plane strain condition, subjected to biaxial tension. Inset shows the stress distribution in region near but not at crack tip extending beyond it a distance small compared to a.*

$$\eta = \eta_0 \sqrt{\frac{2r}{a}} \left(\sin^2 \phi + \frac{a^2}{c^2} \cos^2\phi \right)^{1/4}$$

(*Assumption*—Again, r is small, relative to a.)

Step 4 in Analysis:

Making the substitution, the expression for K in terms of the dimensions and the crack opening of the ellipse is:

$$K = \frac{1}{2} \frac{E}{(1-\nu^2)} \eta_0 \sqrt{\frac{\pi}{a}} \left[\frac{a^2}{c^2} \cos^2\phi + \sin^2\phi \right]^{1/4}$$

Step 5 in Analysis:

Substituting the value for η_0 given by Green and Sneddon (Step 1) gives the desired expression for K, the stress intensity factor in terms of gross stress and crack geometry:

$$K = \frac{\sigma}{\Phi} \sqrt{\pi a} \left(\frac{a^2}{c^2} \cos^2 \phi + \sin^2 \phi \right)^{1/4}$$

Step 6 in Analysis:

The term raised to the one-fourth power determines the variation of K around the ellipse. The stress intensity factor is maximum at the minor diameter of the ellipse, minimum at the major axis, the ratio being $\sqrt{a/c}$. Thus,

At $\phi = \frac{\pi}{2}$, (the end of the minor diameter)

$$K = \frac{\sigma \sqrt{\pi a}}{\Phi}$$

This is the expression previously given minus the correction terms for the front-face free surface and the plastic zone.

(*Assumption*—When these formula are used to compute K_{Ic} , it is assumed that they apply over a length of crack front great enough to include the "sufficiently large volume" of material in which fracture is assumed to be initiated.)

Digressing from the analytical effort for a moment, this is the best place to point out the recommended treatment for a short, deep semi-elliptical crack, for which the end of the semiminor axis lies at the specimen surface. Fracture did not appear to initiate there in our tests, probably because the constraint is low at the free surface. Thus, we we need the expression for stress intensity factor at the end of the semimajor axis of the ellipse, where ϕ equals zero.

At $\phi = 0$, $\qquad K = \frac{\sigma}{\Phi} \sqrt{\pi a} \sqrt{\frac{a}{c}}$

The variation of K around the ellipse, for three crack shapes, is given in Fig. 76.

Correction Factors for K

No. 1 Correction Factor:

Front-face free surface. Correction for the free surface that is normal to the plane of the crack and divides it into a semiellipse is given by Irwin as a 20 per cent increase in K_{Ic}^2 (about $1.10 \times K_{Ic}$). This was taken from earlier work and may be most easily seen by comparing published expressions for K for a through, center crack of length $2a$ and a symmetrical edge-crack of depth, a.[38] Their ratio is

[38] J. E. Srawley and W. F. Brown, Jr., "Fracture Toughness Testing Methods," *Fracture Toughness Testing and Its Applications, ASTM STP 381*, Am. Soc. Testing Mats., 1965, pp. 133–196.

$$\frac{K^2_{\text{edge}}}{K^2_{\text{center}}} = \frac{\tan\dfrac{\pi a}{W} + 0.1 \sin\dfrac{2\pi a}{W}}{\tan\dfrac{\pi a}{W}}$$

For short cracks, that is, small values of a/W, angle, tangent and sine are nearly equal, and

$$\frac{K^2_{\text{edge}}}{K^2_{\text{center}}} = 1.2$$

(*Assumption*—The factor is strictly applicable only to long shallow

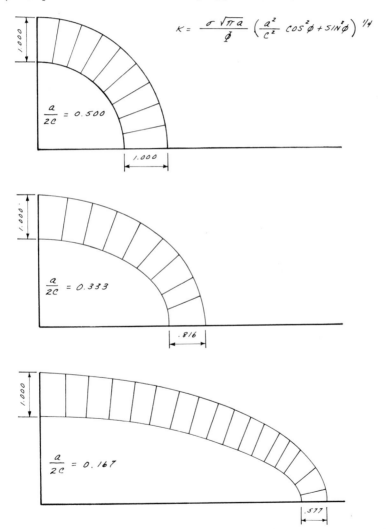

$$K = \frac{\sigma \sqrt{\pi a}}{\phi} \left(\frac{a^2}{c^2} \cos^2\phi + \sin^2\phi \right)^{1/4}$$

FIG. 76—*Variation of stress intensity factor around an ellipse, for three different shapes of crack.*

cracks ($a/c \rightarrow 0$). The effect would be less for larger a/c ratios, but Irwin left the factor constant to compensate for omissioe of the back face correction factor. Paris, on the other hand, applies a front face correction factor to K of $[1 + 0.12 (1 - a/c)]$, or about 1.04 for cracks of normal proportions.[39])

No. 2 Correction Factor:

Back-face free surface. Irwin considered this correction to be small and to be partially compensated for by the overestimate of the correction for the free surface at the cracked face; hence, he did not correct for it. This seems to be a point that needs additional work. Paris[39] reports sizeable correction factors for edge effects in a centrally-cracked finite-width strip. Values from Paris' Table I are plotted in Fig. 77 as the curve labeled "straight crack." Reasoning from that data, one would predict that the back-surface correction for K for a crack for which the a/c ratio approaches zero and the depth equals $\frac{1}{2}$ the plate thickness would be 1.22. The correction is increasing rapidly in this region. Kobayashi[40] shows that the curvature effect of crack-front on the free-surface effect is not very large. From his Table I (which gives values of $1/\Phi$) the effect of the back surface on stress intensity factor at the bottom of a half-depth crack where $a/2c = 0.3$, is to reduce it by 4 per cent. Thus the net effect of the back surface on K is to increase it by a factor of 1.17, in this typical case.

No. 3 Correction Factor:

Plastic flow at the crack tip. This complex problem is treated in the following simplified way. Rewriting the equation from Step 6 (and including the front face correction factor)

$$K_{Ic}^2 = \frac{1.2\pi\sigma^2}{\Phi^2} (a + r_y)$$

This includes the addition of the plastic zone radius to the crack depth. Thinking of K_{Ic} as a measure of fracture toughness and σ as the gross stress at fracture, one sees that this procedure yields a higher fracture toughness value for a material that develops a larger plastic zone.

Computation of r_y is made from the equation for stress distribution normal to plane of crack at the crack tip:

$$\sigma_y = K \sqrt{\frac{1}{2\pi r}}$$

[39] P. C. Paris and G. C. Sih, "Stress Analysis of Cracks," *Fracture Toughness Testing and Its Applications, ASTM STP 381*, Am. Soc. Testing Mats., 1965.
[40] A. S. Kobayashi, M., Ziv., and L. R. Hall, "Approximate Strees Intensity Factor for an Embedded Elliptical Crack Near two Parallel Free Surfaces," *International Journal of Fracture Mechanics*, June, 1965, pp. 81–95.

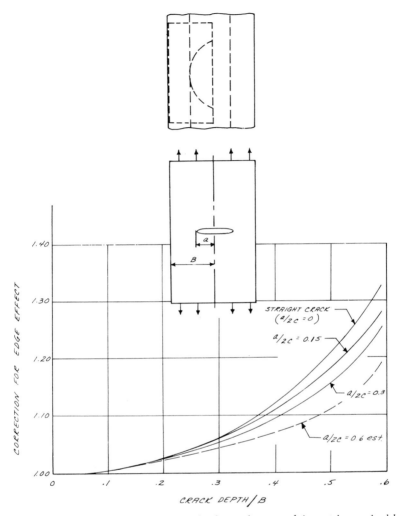

FIG. 77—*Correction for stress intensity factor for a crack in a strip required by the proximity of the edge to the crack tip (from Paris and Kobayashi).*

In a plane stress situation,

$$\sigma_y = \sigma_{\text{YS}}$$

In plane strain, the effect of the two transverse tensions is to raise the yield stress at the edge of the plastic zone.

(*Assumption*—From the 1st ASTM report[41] "The plastic zone appears to the stress field as a region of somewhat relieved normal stress, σ_y, an effect roughly comparable to an extra extension of the crack.")

---

[41] "Special ASTM Committee on Fracture Testing of High Strength Sheet Materials, Report No. 1," *ASTM Bulletin*, Am. Soc. Testing Mats., January, 1960, pp. 29–40.

Irwin uses a factor of $\sqrt{2\sqrt{2}} = 1.68$ for the ratio of yield stresses.[42] Thus, setting $\sigma_y = \sqrt{2\sqrt{2}}\,\sigma_{YS}$, he computes r_y:

$$r_y = \frac{K_{Ic}^2}{4\pi\sqrt{2}\sigma_{YS}^2}$$

Substituting:

$$K_{Ic}^2 = \frac{1.2\pi\sigma^2}{\Phi^2}\left(a + \frac{K_{Ic}^2}{4\pi\sqrt{2}\sigma_{YS}^2}\right)$$

Combining terms:

$$K_{Ic}^2 = \frac{1.2\pi\sigma^2 a}{\Phi^2 - 0.212\,\dfrac{\sigma^2}{\sigma_{YS}^2}}$$

This is Irwin's expression for stress intensity factor at the bottom of a semielliptical crack whose depth is the minor axis of the ellipse. It contains corrections for the front-face free surface and for the plastic zone.

(*Assumption*—Yielding is governed by a maximum shear stress "law." Also, the plane strain case is adequately represented by a notched round, as far as restraint is concerned.)

No. 4 Correction Factor:

Net section effect. To correct for the elevation of stress on the plane containing the crack, caused by the reduction of cross section, K_{Ic} calculated in the usual way should be multiplied by A_{gross}/A_{net}.

It should be stated at the outset that this is not one of the factors considered by Irwin. It does not arise in the analysis of the complete ellipse in an infinite body, nor whenever crack area is a negligible part of the gross. Yet there is always pressure from practical considerations to use small specimens, but the toughness of the material requires the use of large crack sizes to produce fracture at stresses in the elastic range.

A crack affects the strength of a specimen in three ways, and their relative importance depends on crack size relative to specimen size and on the fracture toughness of the material:

1. A crack obviously reduces the specimen cross section; this weakening effect is proportional to the ratio of crack area to specimen gross area. It would be there even if the crack were blunt or if it were ground out.

2. A crack raises the stress required for tensile instability failure of the

---

[42] G. R. Irwin, "Plastic Zone Near a Crack and Fracture Toughness," Seventh Sagamore Ordinance Materials Research Conference, August, 1960.

material near the crack tip because the stress state there constrains flow, thereby strengthening the specimen. In notched rounds, this effect can be large, but in surface-cracked specimens, it is barely noticeable.

3. A crack raises the level of local strain at the crack tip and also raises the flow stress at that point because the constraint develops tri-axial tension, with the result that crack growth may be initiated long before the general level of strain on the net section is high enough to cause tensile instability; hence, the specimen has been weakened by the crack, and the mode of failure is by crack propagation.

In full-size hardware, only the third effect is important. In small specimens, however, the first effect is also significant; hence, it should be subtracted off, and this is easily done by quoting stress values based on the net section, or by multiplying K_{Ic} by $A_{\text{gross}}/A_{\text{net}}$.

Application of Correction Terms to K_{IC} in Anaylsis of Test Results

The conventional treatment of data in section titled "Test Results for Semielliptical Cracks" and Fig. 73 gave K_{Ic} values corrected only for the front-face free surface and the plastic zone. There was a trend with increasing crack size seen in those values, which was downward for the two frangible materials and upward for the two tough ones. In reviewing the derivation of the equation used to compute K_{Ic}, it seemed that two additional corrections were called for: (1) net section effect and (2) effect of the back-face free surface. In addition, some correction for the shape of nonelliptical cracks should be applied, and for short, deep cracks the stress intensity factor should be that at the end of the major axis of the ellipse. The magnitude of each correction to $K_{\text{Ic, conventional}}$ is tabulated in the AFML report[32], but the tables were too long to include here.

With regard to the correction for crack shape, the nonelliptical cracks were described as "cusp," "saddle," "rectangle," "triangle," "irregular," or "incomplete," as illustrated in Fig. 78. Cusps and saddles were assumed to be like very long, shallow cracks ($a/2c = 0$) in obtaining Q values from the nomograph, Fig. 67. For the others, equivalent $a/2c$ values were obtained from crack front curvature measurements. Note that in these cases, a/Q and K_{Ic} will be affected equally.

The correction for the back-face free surface was obtained from Fig. 77. The correction for net section effect has also been discussed in section titled "Stress Intensity Factor K_{Ic} for Surface-Cracked Specimens— Review of Derivation."

The summation of all this corrective effort is given in Fig. 79. For the frangible condition of both alloys, D6-AC *high* and Ti-6Al-4V *high*, the values for $K_{\text{Ic, corrected}}$, are nearly constant with crack size. Actually, they now increase slightly with increasing a/Q, whereas the conventional values of K_{Ic}, plotted in Fig. 80 decreased with crack size. It is not sur-

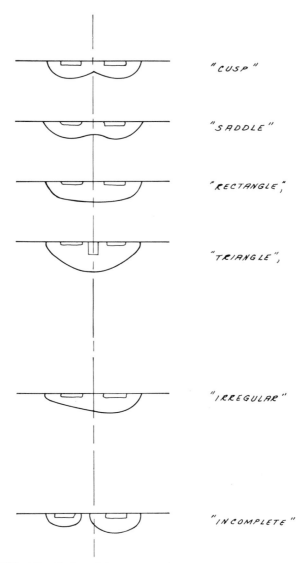

FIG. 78—*Code and descriptive title for nonsemielliptical cracks*

prising, then, that for the tough materials, D6-AC *low* and Ti-6Al-4V *low*, there is an even sharper increase in K_{Ic} with a/Q than before.

The effects of crack shape can be seen by a close scrutiny of the data points for various crack types in Fig. 79. In most cases there does not seem to be a difference between the "normal" and "abnormal" semi-ellipses. Nonelliptical cracks when treated as described, seem to follow the trends fairly well. Note, however, that the correction for crack front curvature affects a/Q and K_{Ic} equally; hence, the "squares" for regular

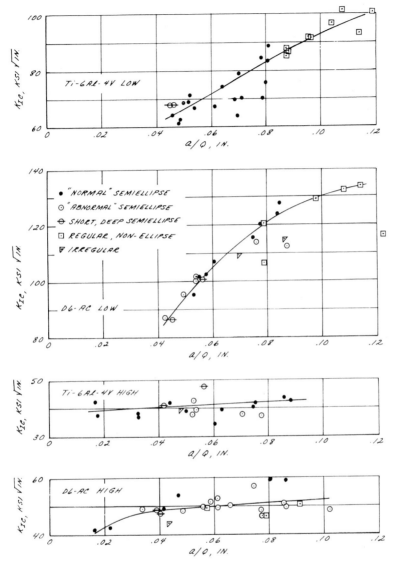

FIG. 79—*Effect of crack size on K_{Ic}, corrected, for all four materials. All crack shapes are included.*

nonellipses are moved both up and to the right. Since the trend is that way, anyway, it is not absolutely clear from this plot that the situation has been improved.

At one time, it was felt that long, shallow cracks degraded strength more than predicted by a/Q, where Q was computed by assuming that $a/2c$ is given with sufficient accuracy by the ratio crack depth/length. It now appears, from the relatively small scatter of the data plotted, in

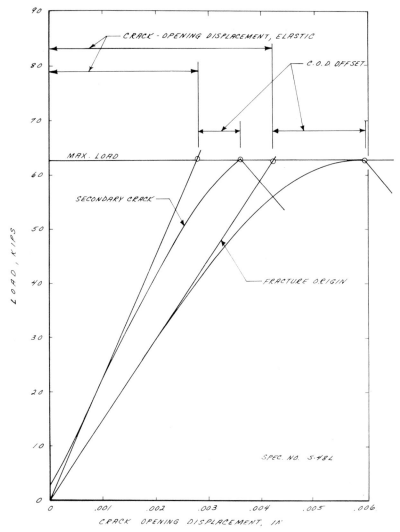

FIG. 80—*Typical test records for a twin-crack specimen, showing measurement of COD offset.*

Fig. 79, that this is not true. The term, Q, does account for crack shape fairly well if the cracks are elliptical. If not, then the $a/2c$ ratio must be obtained from crack front curvature measured over the middle third (approximately) of the crack length.

Effects of Plasticity on the Trends in K_{IC} with Crack Size

Because the trend of K_{Ic} values with crack size was so clearly a function of the toughness of the material, the explanation must lie in the effects of plastic strain at the crack tip. The crack opening displacement

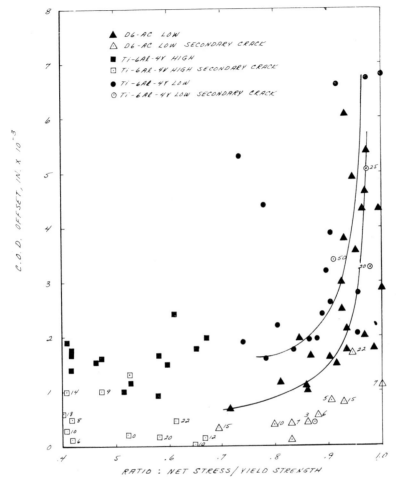

FIG. 81—*Effect of stress level on crack opening displacement offset for all materials except D6-AC HIGH, which had none. Slow growth measurements on the secondary cracks are given in mils.*

record provides some evidence in this regard. A typical record, shown in Fig. 80, has a linear portion, followed by a gradual offset of the curve from the prolongation of the elastic part. This "COD offset" must be evidence of crack growth or plastic flow or both at the crack tip. To try to determine which of these components predominated, data for COD offset are plotted versus the ratio of net stress to yield strength in Fig. 81. Data for the secondary cracks are also shown and the amount of slow growth (in mils) is written beside each data point.

For the two tough materials, the conclusion drawn from Fig. 81 is as follows. Because COD offset is larger for small cracks and is sharply dependent on the stress when it exceeds 90 per cent of the yield strength, the COD offset appears to be a measure of plastic flow at the crack tip. This is borne out by the lack of correlation of the amount of slow growth with the COD offset. More importantly, the amount of slow growth is too small to affect COD offset much in a typical case. Referring to Fig. 80, the linear part of the COD offset at maximum load is about 0.003 in. Crack depth was 0.070 in. Slow growth increased this by only 6 per cent. This should affect COD offset by the same amount, because it is linearly dependent on depth. But this is only a small fraction of the COD offset. Thus, the conclusion is that the COD offset is an indication of development of the plastic zone, which places a limit on the validity of fracture toughness calculations. The data in Fig. 81 shows that this limit should be about 90 per cent of the yield strength.

One possible explanation for the increase in K_{Ic} with increasing values of a/Q lies in the change in plastic constraint that accompanies changes in crack depth. The quality of a metal called fracture toughness may be regarded as its ability to suffer large strains at the crack tip before separation takes place. It is well known that this quality is much affected by the stress state in the process zone, as it is called. (The terms plane stress and plane strain are meant to characterize the degree of constraint but the latter, particularly, is somewhat loosely used and its traditional meaning does not fully define the state of stress in the process zone.) Proximity of the back-face free surface probably has the most effect on the transverse tension in the thickness direction. If so, deep cracks (large a/Q) have less severe constraint at the crack tip, which in turn permits a material to exhibit greater resistance to propagation of a deep crack than a shallow one. This hypothesis is offered as a basis for further work on the effect of crack size on K_{Ic}.

To relate this work to the recommendations of Committee E-24, values of the factor $2.5\ K_{Ic}^2/\sigma_{YS}^2$ are tabulated below. The specimen thickness was 0.25 in. in this program, and the maximum crack depth was 0.125 in.

Material	K_{Ic}, conventional ksi $\sqrt{\text{in.}}$	σ_{YS}, ksi	$2.5\ K_{Ic}^2/\sigma_{YS}^2$, in.
D6-AC *high*	45	249	0.08
Ti-6Al-4V *high*	35	160	0.12
D6-AC *low*	90	212	0.45
Ti-6Al-4V *low*	65	154	0.44

Only in the D6-AC *high* were the crack depths definitely greater than $2.5\ K_{Ic}^2/\sigma_{YS}^2$; hence, the test results have not yielded any "valid K_{Ic}" values for the two tough materials and only a few for the Ti-6Al-4V *high* with the largest cracks. Where greater metal thickness is available and the tests are feasible, perhaps the use of greater specimen thickness and larger crack sizes is the proper solution—perhaps it is the only solution. Where greater metal thickness is not available, some other means of evaluation is required.

Conclusions and Recommendations

Surface cracks induced by cyclic bending of the specimen to grow a fatigue crack from a point source were found to be semiellipses; hence, this assumption in the conventional analysis of results is valid. More specifically, measurements of each crack revealed that the curvature in the central region was that of an ellipse in which the major axis was crack length, $2c$, and the semiminor axis was crack depth, a.

In studies of the effects of crack shape, it was found that the quantity, a/Q, the "normalized crack depth" correlated the effects of crack shape quite well. Even the regular, nonelliptical cracks were characterized fairly well as to their severity, if crack front curvature was measured to determine an equivalent $a/2c$ value for use in obtaining Q. The "cusps" etc. whose crack fronts were convex were considered to have equivalent $a/2c$ ratios equal to zero, and the results correlated fairly well.

The major problem in correlating the results concerned the treatment of effects of crack size. The term a/Q is the conventional measure of this, but K_{Ic} values were not constant with size. Furthermore, the trend in K_{Ic} with increasing a/Q was downward for the two materials in the frangible condition, but it was upward for the two materials in the tough, *low*, yield strength condition. It was found possible to correct the downward trend in K_{Ic} for the frangible materials by applying two corrections to the conventional values of K_{Ic}. The first correction was for the increase of stress intensity factor caused by the proximity of the back face to the crack tip. The second correction was for the net section effect. However, when these correction factors were applied to the conventional values of K_{Ic} for the tough materials, they increased with crack size more rapidly than before.

As a result of the rather close scrutiny of the test results for crack size particularly, we do not recommend the writing of a specification or test standard for the general use of the surface-cracked specimen to measure fracture toughness. We believe that the correction factors suggested for K_{Ic} are proper, but no claim can be made that they will give a constant value of K_{Ic} for a given material, independent of crack size. Yet the basic reason for use of a K_{Ic} value to characterize fracture toughness is that it permits the correlation of stress to flaw size.

The surface-cracked specimen can be used effectively in specific hardware programs where the flaw size can be estimated, where the flaw geometry resembles surface cracks, and where material thicknesses are known and can be used in the test specimen as well.

Messrs. Brown and Srawley—Mr. Randall is to be complimented on a very informative investigation of the surface-crack specimen. The results he obtained illustrate the complexities associated with the stress analysis of this specimen and serve to emphasize that it is not suitable for general use in K_{Ic} testing. Further experimental work of the type described by Mr. Randall should be encouraged.

S. R. Novak[43] *and S. T. Rolfe*[43]—The authors are to be congratulated for their successful efforts in establishing test procedures for determining K_{Ic} values of high-strength metals. In keeping with the importance of this problem, an extensive program to develop quantitative information on the fracture toughness of steels and weldments is currently in progress at the U.S. Steel Applied Research Laboratory. Among other tests the four-point, slow-bend specimen (incorporating side notches) is being used to measure the fracture toughness of steels having yield strengths

TABLE 8—*Properties and geometry of typical steels investigated.*

Steel	σ_{YS} (0.2% offset), ksi	CVN at +80 F, ft·lb	W,[a] in.	a, in.	$W/(K_{Ic}/\sigma_{YS})^2$,[c]	B,[b] in.	$B/(K_{Ic}/\sigma_{YS})^2$,[c]
18Ni (250) A-538 Grade B.	246	16	4.0	2.08	32.0	1.92	15.4
18Ni (200)	192	25	4.0	1.28	12.9	1.82	5.9
18Ni (190)	187	58	4.0	1.45	5.0	1.97	2.47
12Ni-5Cr-3Mo (induction vacuum melt)	186	65	5.0	1.44	3.2	1.89	1.20
5Ni-Cr-Mo-V	149	89	8.0	2.16	2.3	1.94	0.55
4147 A-372 Class V—Type E	137	26	2.3	0.75	3.0	0.50	0.64
T-1 A-517 Grade F	110	62	6.0	2.60	2.3	1.84	0.71

[a] W = specimen depth.
[b] B = specimen width.
[c] Apparent K_{Ic} value.

from 30 to 250 ksi, and where applicable, to determine the plane-strain stress-intensity parameter, K_{Ic}. As proposed by ASTM Committee E-24, the applicability of such testing to the determination of valid K_{Ic} values would be limited to tests in which the load-deflection records exhibit more than a minimum amount of popin and less than a maximum amount of deviation from linearity prior to popin. The minimum popin step and maximum deviation from linearity are related to the plastic-zone size at popin as defined in "Criteria for Analysis of Popin Records," in the *Sixth Progress Report of ASTM Committee E-24.*

The load deflection records for K_{Ic} tests of various steels, Table 8, are being analyzed using the proposed criteria, and the analysis indicates that the proposed criteria are believed to be more restrictive than necessary to determine valid K_{Ic} values. These tests were conducted using

[43] Applied Research Laboratory, U.S. Steel Corp., Monroeville, Pa.

four-point loading with pins at all loading points, and the crack-opening displacement gage described in the *Sixth Progress Report*. In addition, load-displacement records were obtained as a check on the COD records.

Typical data taken from these studies, Table 9, show that specimens prepared from 2-in.-thick plate of 18Ni (250) maraging steel just meet the deviation from linearity requirement in the load-crack-opening displacement record even though such specimens were more than six times larger than the minimum size specimen currently considered adequate for valid K_{Ic} testing. Similar large size specimens prepared from 18Ni (200) maraging steel at a geometry greater than twice the minimum

TABLE 9—*Fracture properties of steels investigated.*

Steel	K_{Ic} , ksi in.$^{1/2}$,[a]	K_{Ic}/σ_{YS}, in.$^{1/2}$,[a]	$\sigma n_f/\sigma_{YS}$,[b]	r_y in.,[c]	Deviation from Linearity	
					Proposed ASTM (max) Criteria, $\Delta v_i/v_i$,[d]	Actual Experimental Value, $\Delta v_i/v_i$
18Ni (250) A-538 Grade B.	87	0.35	0.40	0.02	0.055	0.041[e]
18Ni (200)...............	107	0.56	0.55	0.05	0.035	0.082[e]
18Ni (190)...............	167	0.89	0.90	0.13	0.037	0.243[e]
12Ni-5Cr-3Mo...........	233	1.25	1.09	0.25	0.034	0.214[f]
5Ni-Cr-Mo-V............	279	1.87	1.36	0.56	0.034	0.222[f]
4147 A-372 Class V— Type E.....................	121	0.88	1.17	0.12	0.035	0.256[f]
T-1 A-517 Grade F.......	177	1.61	1.33	0.41	0.044	0.129

[a] Apparent K_{Ic} value.
[b] Nominal fracture stress = Mc/I
[c] Plane stress plastic zone size = $(1/2\pi)(K_{Ic}/\sigma_{YS})^2$
[d] $\Delta v_i/v_i$ = Maximum permissible deviation from linearity $\leqq$ H/50 (see *Sixth Progress Report*).
[e] Complete failure at popin (maximum load).
[f] Popin just below maximum load.

specimen size were found to exhibit average deviations in linearity that were approximately 100 per cent in excess of that permissible. Additional specimens at the minimum size from specially processed 18Ni (190) maraging steel with K_{Ic}/σ_{YS} values of 0.89 were found to have average deviations from linearity on the order of 500 per cent in excess of that allowable according to the proposed criterion, Table 9.

The K_{Ic} values for these three steels are believed to be representative for these materials, and all requirements for valid K_{Ic} measurements such as specimen size requirements, stress at popin, popin step, etc. were satisfied, except the proposed deviation from linearity criteria, even for relatively thick plates (2 in.). Thus, these results indicate that the proposed criteria for deviation from linearity may be too restrictive.

Because of the increasing emphasis on the use of lower-strength higher-toughness steels, slow-bend tests have also been conducted on steels having yield strengths well below 200 ksi, Table 8. Although these steels are not covered by the proposed *First Progress Report*, the results were analyzed using the same criteria.

In these tests, all procedures currently being advanced by the authors for valid K_{Ic} measurements were followed, although the specimen sizes, Table 8, were somewhat undersized according to the suggested criteria because of the high K_{Ic}/σ_{YS} ratios of these steels. The results of these tests, Table 9, using steels having a range of strength levels indicate that the deviation from linearity requirement proposed for K_{Ic} testing of materials with strength-to-density ratios of greater than 700,000 in. does not necessarily hold for the higher toughness materials at the lower strength levels.

In summary, it appears that only steels with low toughness to strength ratios ($K_{Ic}/\sigma_{YS} \leqq 0.35$) satisfy the proposed deviation from linearity requirements, Table 9. The data presented in this discussion suggest that the criteria for permissible deviation from linearity proposed by the authors not only may be too restrictive for many existing steels but also may be too restrictive for lower strength steels, as well as for any newer, tougher steels with yield strengths greater than 200 ksi currently under development.

Messrs. Brown and Srawley—We do not disagree with Messrs. Novak and Rolfe in their suggestion that the proposed criteria for analysis of load-displacement records is not useful for steels having $(K_{Ic}/\sigma_{YS})^2$ ratios above those for alloys reported in this paper. Our primary purpose was to illustrate how the problem of specimen design and data analysis could be approached rather than to provide a procedure that would be applicable over a wide range of alloy toughness and strength level.

Steels of complex composition such as the 18Ni and 12Ni maraging types in their tougher conditions often exhibit considerable deviation from linearity before popin. This behavior is associated with a laminated structure which often characterizes these alloys. If the segregation responsible for the lamination is especially severe no distinct popin is observed and the K_{Ic} test is difficult to interpret in terms of the bulk fracture properties of the specimen.

We have no experience in testing steel with yield strengths well below 200 ksi such as the last three alloys in the discussers' tables. However, we are not surprised that large deviations from linearity were observed for these alloys. Furthermore, we wonder whether popin just below maximum load (as indicated in Table 9) has the same significance as that observed for the higher strength alloys we tested.

In our opinion we are just starting on a long road which, if we are patient, will eventually lead to a comprehensive approach to the engineering fracture of metallic materials. This road is full of pitfalls and disappointments, not the least of which is represented by the problem of interpreting load-displacement records. It is now clear that many materials will not exhibit popin behavior sufficiently distinct to permit establishing a criteria for minimum size of the indication nor will increasing the specimen size increase the distinctness of the popin. Under these circumstances an empirical method of analysis must be developed. We would suggest the load for K_{Ic} calculation be established by the intersection between the load-displacement curve and the secant whose slope represents some fixed relative crack extension. The worth of this suggestion can only be established by a systematic test program such as outlined in this paper.

THIS PUBLICATION is one of many issued by the American Society for Testing and Materials in connection with its work of promoting knowledge of the properties of materials and developing standard specifications and tests for materials. Much of the data result from the voluntary contributions of many of the country's leading technical authorities from industry, scientific agencies, and government.

Over the years the Society has published many technical symposiums, reports, and special books. These may consist of a series of technical papers, reports by the ASTM technical committees, or compilations of data developed in special Society groups with many organizations cooperating. A list of ASTM publications and information on the work of the Society will be furnished on request.